Essential Everyday Reading

Kathy Sammis

J. WESTON

WALCH
PUBLISHER
Portland, Maine

User's Guide
to
Walch Reproducible Books

As part of our general effort to provide educational materials which are as practical and economical as possible, we have designated this publication a "reproducible book." The designation means that purchase of the book includes purchase of the right to limited reproduction of all pages on which this symbol appears:

Here is the basic Walch policy: We grant to individual purchasers of this book the right to make sufficient copies of reproducible pages for use by all students of a single teacher. This permission is limited to a single teacher, and does not apply to entire schools or school systems, so institutions purchasing the book should pass the permission on to a single teacher. Copying of the book or its parts for resale is prohibited.

Any questions regarding this policy or requests to purchase further reproduction rights should be addressed to:

Permissions Editor
J. Weston Walch, Publisher
321 Valley Street • P. O. Box 658
Portland, Maine 04104-0658

Certified Chain of Custody
SUSTAINABLE FORESTRY INITIATIVE
Promoting Sustainable Forest Management
www.sfiprogram.org

SGS-SFI/COC-US09/5501

1   2   3   4   5   6   7   8   9   10

ISBN 0-8251-2910-9

Copyright © 1997
J. Weston Walch, Publisher
P. O. Box 658 • Portland, Maine 04104-0658
Printed in the United States of America

Contents

Unit 1. Around the House 1

Unit 2. Automotive 15

Unit 3. Banking and Finance 31

Unit 4. Out in Public 45

UNIT 5. CONSUMERISM **61**

UNIT 6. FOOD **75**

UNIT 7. ENTERTAINMENT **89**

UNIT 8. HEALTH AND PERSONAL CARE **103**

UNIT 9. POPULAR PRESS **115**

To the Teacher

Essential Everyday Reading is designed to give students practice in developing the reading skills they need to function effectively in daily life. We are all bombarded daily by written information that we have to read—often very quickly—to accomplish myriad everyday activities: Use an ATM, board a bus, do the laundry, pump gas, fix a quick meal, relieve a sore throat, make a phone call, find assistance. This may be the video age, but you still have to be able to read to choose which video to rent or which movie theater to go to at what time.

Essential Everyday Reading helps your students develop these needed reading skills by presenting a variety of real-life reading selections from signs, labels, and instructions they are likely to encounter frequently. The exercises that accompany each reading selection help the students read for comprehension and also develop the habit of reading and understanding directions for products and appliances they are about to use and for activities they're about to engage in. Ability and willingness to follow directions allow a person to avoid not only many minor inconveniences and unnecessary expenses but also serious personal injury or even death in some cases.

The selections in *Essential Everyday Reading* are grouped into nine categories. Each unit except the ninth begins with a vocabulary activity to familiarize students with words that may be new to them. The teacher section also includes a list of additional vocabulary words for each unit that you may wish to preteach to your students. The exercises for each reading selection promote reading skill and comprehension by requiring students to use details and facts from the selection to answer questions in varied forms such as true-false, multiple choice, and anecdotal situations. The What Do You Think? exercises guide students toward an understanding of the main idea and toward a wider application of the concepts presented in the reading selection. All exercises are written in simple, easy-to-read language that helps to clarify the generally higher-level language of the real-life selections. The teacher section also includes an answer key for all the exercises.

Students will sometimes be under time pressure to read selections like those presented here—for example, the ATM directions and the directions for boarding a bus and paying the fare. To give students practice in dealing with reading in such situations, several of the reading selections have a brief, italicized introduction putting the students—if they choose—into a time-pressure scenario. You might also have students time themselves for these types of readings.

Through practice with these reading selections, your students should improve their ability to deal with the many reading situations they face every day, gain confidence in that ability, and develop the sometimes vital habit of reading signs, instructions, and directions.

ADDITIONAL VOCABULARY

You may wish to preteach these terms in addition to those presented in each unit opening exercise.

Unit 1. Around the House

abrasive	inconspicuous	obstruction
antidote	infested	operable
flammable (*see Unit 4*)	intact	polyester
inaccessible	manual (*n.*)	precautionary
inconsistent	nonporous	pressure gauge

Unit 2. Automotive

antenna	emission	transmission
chrome	grade	

Unit 3. Banking and Finance

business day	financial institution	money market
credit line	impose	two-party check

Unit 4. Out in Public

access	exceed	selector
accommodate	fecal deposits	solvent
area code	intensive	spigot
bureau	preparatory	step well
cardiac	regulation	surgical
dyeing	restrained	toll free

Unit 5. Consumerism

agencies
aluminum
bureau
catalog
caution
clearance
collectibles

consumer
environmental
hazardous (*see Unit 1*)
invisible
merchandise
nonprofit
perspective

postal
priority
refuge
suicide
tinting

Unit 6. Food

ample
appliance
cavity
cholesterol
dietary fiber
farina
fat

hydrogenated
interlock
monounsaturated
polyunsaturated
saturated
scalloped
semolina

technician
tempered
usable
vinaigrette
visibility

Unit 7. Entertainment

alien
commercial
container
lethal

patron
periodically
protective
shutter

telephoto/zoom lens
terminator
versatility

Unit 8. Health and Personal Care

abrasion
accompanied
application
chafed
conscious
discontinue
dissolve
expiration

formula
incinerate (*see Unit 1*)
inhale (*see Unit 1*)
intentional
irritated/irritation
   (*see Unit 1*)
medication
nausea

occasional
overdose
resistant
straddle
tamper
thoroughly
tingling

ANSWER KEY

Unit 1. Around the House

Vocabulary

1. hazardous
2. contaminate
3. irritation
4. ventilation
5. incinerate
6. inhale
7. physician
8. disinfect
9. flush
10. extinguisher
11. maintenance
12. interval
13. residue
14. discharge
15. vapor
16. adequate

All-purpose Cleaner

1. (a) no scrubbing or rinsing required (easy to use)

   (b) doesn't harm most kitchen and bathroom surfaces (contains no harsh abrasives or acids)

2. sinks, tubs, tiles, toilets, showers, floors (*name five*)

3. Clean tiles first, then spray to thoroughly wet.

4. mold, mildew

5. (a) Wipe right off.

   (b) 15–20 seconds

   (c) 10 minutes

   (d) 3 minutes

6. Wash thoroughly with soap and water. Talk to a doctor if your skin becomes irritated.

7.–10. *Answers will vary.*

Clothing Labels

1. c, d
2. a, d
3. a, c, d
4. a, b, d
5. suit jacket
6. sweater, blouse
7. robe
8. sweater, suit jacket
9. robe, blouse, tank top, sweatshirt (if undecorated)
10. sweater, sweatshirt, blouse, suit jacket, tank top
11. *Answers will vary.*

Fire Extinguisher

1. Write to the manufacturer for a replacement.

2. If you test it, you must have it recharged before it will work again.

3. Be sure the pressure gauge is in operating range.

4. Check pressure gauge. Be sure nozzle isn't obstructed. Check that ring pull pin is intact. Inspect monthly.

5. 2, 4, 3, 1

6. Wash out your eyes with a steady, strong flow of water.

7. Have it recharged right away.

8.–9. *Answers will vary.*

Roach and Ant Killer

1. cockroaches, ants, other crawling insects

2. (a) cracks and baseboards

   (b) trails, entry points (windows, doors)

   (c) infested areas

3. humans, pets, food, utensils, dishes, food preparation areas, plants, shrubs (*name five*)

4. Remove children and pets from area.

5. Wash hands thoroughly with soap and water. Keep children and pets away until area is dry.

6. Get medical care right away (call poison control, doctor; go to emergency room).

7.–9. *Answers will vary.*

Unit 2. Automotive

Vocabulary

1. nozzle
2. receipt
3. authorize
4. chassis
5. specify
6. signature
7. engage
8. compartment
9. vehicle
10. bay
11. negligence
12. fee
13. install
14. rotate
15. credit
16. groove

Gas Pump

1. regular unleaded, cash price
   ultra unleaded, credit price

2. Turn off engine.

3. Enter ATM number.
   Press Clear/Cancel.

4. 5, 7, 3, 1, 8, 4, 6, 2

5. Pay inside.

6. Use a credit card.

7. Use an ATM card.

8.–9. *Answers will vary.*

Auto Repair

1. (a) False

   (b) True

   (c) False

   (d) True

   (e) True

   (f) False

   (g) False

   (h) True

   (i) False

   (j) False

2. It has not specified what this
   charge is for.

3. quantity, number, automatic
   transmission, lubrication, air
   conditioning, alignment

4. *Answers will vary.*

Auto Service Notice

1. b, c, g

2. flat pricing

3. menu pricing

4.–5. *Answers will vary.*

Tire Changing

1. Place heavy objects like wooden
   blocks or rocks in front of and
   behind the wheels on the side of
   the car opposite the jack.

2.

   Clockwise   Counterclockwise

3. (a) Dangerous—car can shift
       while jacked up on soft
       sand.

   (b) Safe

   (c) Dangerous—need to look at
       owner's manual to find
       strong points for jacking.

   (d) Safe

   (e) Dangerous—loosen wheel
       nuts only before jacking up;
       don't want tire to fall off
       while jacking car up.

   (f) Dangerous—don't overex-
       tend the jack; raise only as
       high as needed to remove
       tire.

4.–5. *Answers will vary.*

Car Wash

1. antennas, mirrors, loose chrome, clearcoat or polyglycol seal finishes
2. foam bath, undercarriage, wheel scrub, hot wax
3. b, c, e.
4. recreational vehicles and campers; for heat and cooking
5. Fill up with gasoline also.
6. your fault
7.–9. *Answers will vary.*

Unit 3. Banking and Finance

Vocabulary

1. deposit
2. loan
3. account
4. verification
5. withdrawal
6. transferred
7. checkout
8. application
9. minimum
10. identification
11. express
12. transaction
13. balance
14. waive
15. interest
16. varies

Bank Forms

1. deposit or loan payment
2. savings, checking, money market account
3. loan payment, payment to reduce credit line debit
4. cash or checks
5. more than 25 bills; coins
6. no
7. Thursday
8. No—all loan payments are credited the next business day, so your payment is one day late.
9. cash, bank check, or transfer to another account
10. *Answers will vary.*

Check-Cashing Policy and Procedures

1. (a) service desk, check-cashing card, plus two more ID's
   (b) service desk, check-cashing card
   (c) checkout, check-cashing card
   (d) service desk, check-cashing card
   (e) service desk, check-cashing card
   (f) service desk, check-cashing card plus two more ID's
2. a
3. c, d
4. a bounced check—one that you cashed but that was returned because the account it was drawn on didn't have enough funds to cover it
5.–6. *Answers will vary.*

Checking and Savings Accounts

1. (a) NOW
   (b) Personal, NOW
   (c) Basic
   (d) NOW
   (e) Basic, Personal, NOW
   (f) Personal
   (g) Personal, NOW
   (h) Basic
   (i) Basic, Personal
   (j) Basic
   (k) NOW

2. (a) Holiday Club
   (b) Passbook
   (c) Statement
   (d) Holiday Club
   (e) Statement
   (f) Passbook
   (g) Passbook
   (h) Passbook
   (i) Statement
   (j) Holiday Club

3.–4. *Answers will vary.*

ATM Directions

1. Insert ATM card.
2. Select Balance Inquiry at Screen 4.
3. (a) Withdrawal
   (b) From Checking
   (c) 20
4. maybe; Screen 3
5. yes; Screen 9

6. (a) Deposit
   (b) nothing
   (c) 15
7. Enter personal ID number. Use the numbered keypad.
8. no; Screen 6
9. Press Cancel.
10.–11. *Answers will vary.*

Unit 4. Out in Public

Vocabulary

1. dial
2. flammable
3. detergent
4. fabric
5. fare
6. prohibited
7. register
8. confirmation
9. maximum
10. sibling
11. smolder
12. conversation
13. terminal
14. scroll
15. resume
16. emergency

Metro Bus Service

1. (a) 50¢
   (b) 50¢
   (c) $1.15
   (d) $1.15
   (e) 50¢
   (f) 50¢
   (g) $2.30
   (h) $2.30
2. $4
3. a, b, d, f
4. *Answers will vary.*

Pay Phone Directions

1. Dial the number.
2. Call Repair, 1-555-1611.
3. 1+Number
4. O+Number (Person-to-Person)
5. O+Number+calling card number
6. #+Number
7. O
8. O+Number (Collect)
9. 1+Area Code+Number
10. O+Number (wait for operator)
11. 1-555-1212
12.–13. *Answers will vary.*

Hospital Visiting Hours

1. No; on weekdays the Psychiatric Unit opens at 6 P.M.
2. yes
3. yes
4. No; ony immediate family can visit.
5. Yes
6. No; only immediate family can visit.
7. yes
8. yes
9. No; only siblings may visit.
10. No; the Medical and Surgical units are closed between 2 and 6 P.M.
11. yes
12.–13. *Answers will vary.*

Self-service Laundry

1. b, c, f, h, i
2. 5, 3, 1, 4, 2, 6
3.–4. *Answers will vary.*

Campground Use Rules

1. Only one camping setup is allowed per campsite, not three.

2. Only one visiting party is allowed per campsite, and only two vehicles per campsite, including the campers themselves.

3. Quiet is required after 10 P.M.

4. Campers are required to dispose of their waste themselves, not leave it at the registration booth.

5. Campers must check out by 11 A.M.

6. Campers are not allowed to set up after 10 P.M.

7. Use of chain saws and cutting of trees are prohibited.

8. They have stayed too long; maximum length of stay is 14 nights.

9. Only two vehicles are allowed per campsite; they have three.

10. Visitors are allowed only until 8 P.M.

11. *Answers will vary.*

Computer Search Directions

1. **F1**: at the Title? prompt to find the title of a book
   F2: at the Title? prompt to find a subject
   F3: to scroll through the titles/call numbers you have found
   F4: to halt the scroll
   F5: to get a message about starting a new search
   F6: to start a new search after reading the **F5** message
   Enter: to start over if you make a mistake
   Esc: to escape from the current screen; to get back to the Title? prompt

2. when Title? appears on the screen

3. Inquire at the Information Desk on Level 2.

4. It is the book's individual Dewey Decimal (or other system) number; books are shelved in order according to these numbers.

5. fiction; shelved alphabetically by author's last name

6. Press the **Esc** key.

7. Use another terminal that allows an author search; use the card catalog.

8. escape; to escape from the screen you are currently in

9. a list of titles for that subject

Unit 5. Consumerism

Vocabulary

1. radius
2. nominal
3. redeem
4. beverage
5. reject
6. automatic
7. certificate
8. eligible
9. guarantee
10. partial
11. crisis
12. welfare
13. fraud
14. anonymous
15. abuse
16. unusual

Service Desk Information

1. (a) yes
   (b) yes
   (c) no
   (d) yes
   (e) yes
   (f) no
   (g) no
   (h) yes
   (i) yes
   (j) yes
2. Tuesday
3. Thursday (too late for Monday delivery)
4. Saturday
5.–6. *Answers will vary.*

Bottle and Can Recycling

1. 2, 4, 3, 1
2. color of square to press; plastics go in bottom end first
3. (a) aluminum can machine
   (b) bottle return window
   (c) bottle return window
   (d) aluminum can machine
   (e) aluminum can machine
4.–8. *Answers will vary.*

Sweepstakes Notice

1. (a) False
   (b) False
   (c) True
   (d) False
   (e) True
   (f) True
   (g) True
   (h) False
2. uses boldface, centered capital letters
3.–5. *Answers will vary.*

Classified Ads

1. (a) 876-9500
   (b) 337-5679
   (c) Day Street
   (d) 977-4675, Lincoln Street
   (e) High Street #32
   (f) 929-3030

   989-2233
   High Street #32
   (i) Day Street, Lincoln Street
   (j) 999-8484
   (k) Grant Road, High Street #32
   (l) Grant Road, High Street #233, Lincoln Street

2. (a) miscellaneous
   (b) with
   (c) inch/inches
   (d) excellent

   (e) feet/foot
   (f) equipment
   (g) refrigerator

   3.–5. *Answers will vary.*

Telephone Help Lines

1. Animal Refuge League
2. Meals on Wheels
3. Overeaters Anonymous
4. AIDS line
5. Housing Authority
6. Consumer Fraud Bureau
7. Alcoholics Anonymous
8. Rape Crisis
9. Adult & Child Abuse Hot Line
10. Hazardous Substances Spills
11. Kids to Kids
12. ASPCA
13. Planned Parenthood
14. Food Stamps
15. Department of Environmental Protection
16. Suicide Prevention

17.–18. *Answers will vary.*

Unit 6. Food

Vocabulary

1. gelatin
2. dissolve
3. set
4. ingredient
5. invert
6. casserole
7. simmer
8. nutrition
9. defrost
10. utensil
11. automatic
12. requirement
13. restaurant
14. sautéed
15. entree
16. operation

Restaurant Menu

1. folded-over pizza crust stuffed with various ingredients
2. lobster or crab sandwich
3. chef's salad
4. tossed or Greek salad, veggie sub, Italian or Greek calzone, burrito, eggplant lasagna
5. chips
6. cup of chowder or soup of the day
7. tossed salad, turkey avocado sandwich, lobster and crab sandwiches
8. onions, mushrooms, feta cheese
9. cheapest: small tossed or Greek salad; most expensive: lobster sandwich
10.–11. *Answers will vary.*

Fast-food Menu

1. most expensive: chili or double with cheese; cheapest: regular
2. $3.68
3. pepper steak
4. small French fries
5. (a) no
   (b) yes
   (c) yes
   (d) no
6. *Answers will vary.*

Gelatin Dessert Directions

1. (a) 2 cups (1 boiling, 1 cold)
   (b) $1\frac{3}{4}$ cups (1 boiling, $\frac{3}{4}$ cold)
   (c) $1\frac{1}{4}$ cups ($\frac{3}{4}$ boiling, $\frac{1}{2}$ cold) plus ice cubes to make $1\frac{1}{4}$ cups ice and water
2. (a) 3 hours
   (b) Directions don't tell you this.
3. If you were in a hurry; ready to eat in only 30 minutes.
4. Fresh or frozen pineapple or kiwi fruit.
5. *Answers will vary.*

Scalloped Potato Directions

1. (a) microwave
   (b) oven
   (c) oven, microwave
   (d) stove top
   (e) microwave
   (f) oven
   (g) stove top
   (h) microwave
   (i) stove top
   (j) oven, microwave
   (k) oven
2. (a) 30 to 35 minutes
   (b) 30 minutes
   (c) 9 to 10 minutes
3. When they are tender.
4. *Answers will vary.*

Nutritional Information and Ingredients

1. (a) 2 Tbsp (32 grams), 2 oz
       (56 grams)
   (b) 200 each
   (c) 7 grams each
   (d) 5 grams, 42 grams
   (e) 25%, 2%
   (f) 0% each
   (g) 120 mg, 0 mg

2. spaghetti
3. spaghetti
4. peanut butter
5. peanut butter (dextrose)
6. vitamins A, B, C
7. calcium, iron
8.–9. *Answers will vary.*

Microwave Oven

1. a, d, e, g, i
2. 6, 4, 7, 1, 5, 3, 2

3.–4. *Answers will vary.*

Unit 7. Entertainment

Vocabulary

1. accompanied
2. appropriate
3. repetitive
4. temporarily
5. permanent
6. additional
7. process
8. subdued
9. exposure
10. stationary
11. format
12. ensure
13. deterioration
14. compatible
15. videocassette
16. guardian

Video Arcade

1. 2, 5, 3, 1, 4
2. being hit by an enemy laser beam
3. colliding with an enemy
4. by hitting the enemy Mother Ship

5.   1,500
     1,000
     –500
     10,000
     –600
     500
     2,000
     13,900 Total

6.–7. *Answers will vary.*

Movie Listings

1. (a) Monday through Friday
   (b) Saturday and Sunday
   (c) Evenings
   (d) Matinees
2. (a) *Jurassic Park II*
   (b) *Barney!*
   (c) *Batman Returns, Lethal Terminator*
   (d) *Batman Returns, Kidnapped, From the Heart, Lethal Terminator, Jurassic Park II*

   (e) *From the Heart, White Fang, Wilderness Trail*
   (f) *Kidnapped, Lethal Terminator, Nightmare on Elm Street XV, Wayne's World Goes Wild, Alien Planet*
   (g) Everything except *Barney!, Lethal Terminator,* and *Kidnapped.*
   (h) *Lethal Terminator*

3.–6. *Answers will vary.*

Video Store

1. (a) True
   (b) True
   (c) False
   (d) True
   (e) False
   (f) True
   (g) True
   (h) False
2. (a) $10

   (b) $11
   (c) $3
   (d) $5
   (e) $2
   (f) $5
   (g) $10
   (h) $3

3.–4. *Answers will vary.*

Film—Using and Developing

1. (a) 200 speed
   (b) 1600 speed
   (c) 100 speed
   (d) 400 speed
   (e) 100 speed
   (f) 400 or 1600 speed
2. (a) True
   (b) False
   (c) True

3. (a) 4" × 6" double prints or 3½" × 5" double prints
   (b) 4" × 6" single prints or 3½" × 5" single prints
   (c) 4" × 6" single prints **in album** or 4" × 6" single prints **in album**
   (d) DOS/Windows, Macintosh, or Power Mac

4.–6. *Answers will vary.*

Videocassette Care

1. Check a, b, d, e, h, j.
2. Yes; you can try adjusting the tracking switch on your machine.

3.–5. *Answers will vary.*

Unit 8. Health and Personal Care

Vocabulary

1. consult
2. effective
3. avoid
4. ingestion
5. mousse
6. dispense
7. inhale
8. lozenge
9. physician
10. persist
11. accidental
12. abdomen
13. thrust
14. ointment
15. administer
16. exceed

Cold Sore Ointment

1. cold sore, fever blister, sun blister
2. cracked/severely dry lips
3. abrasions, cuts, scrapes, burns, razor nicks, chafed or irritated skin
4. mosquitoes, black flies, sand fleas, chiggers
5. tingling, pain, itching
6. three to four times a day
7. Flush thoroughly with water and get medical help.
8. Get medical help or call a poison control center immediately.
9. deep or puncture wounds, serious burns, rash, infection, large sore area

10.–11. *Answers will vary.*

Hairstyling Mousse

1. b, c, e, f, h
2. 25 to 30 times
3. yes; labeled Extra Control.
4. beautifully glowing, with a soft natural touch

5.–6. *Answers will vary.*

Throat Lozenges

1. (a) False
   (b) True
   (c) False
   (d) False
   (e) True
   (f) False
   (g) True
   (h) True
   (i) True
   (j) False

2. Call if sore throat is severe, persists for more than two days, or is accompanied or followed by fever, headache, rash, nausea, vomiting, or difficulty breathing.

3. See if sore mouth symptoms do not improve in seven days.

4.–5. *Answers will vary.*

First Aid for Choking Victims

1. Be sure the person is choking.

2. c

3. 6, 1, 3, 5, 2, 7, 4

4. Turn the victim onto his or her back. Be sure to turn victim to the side and clear out mouth if victim vomits.

5. Perform the Heimlich maneuver on yourself by pressing your own fist into your abdomen or by pressing your abdomen against the edge of a sink, hard chair, or railing.

6.–7. *Answers will vary.*

Unit 9. Popular Press

Table of Contents

1. Fashion

2. Food and Health

3. Features

4. no

5. yes

6. Fiction: "Running Away to Home"

7. "Hot Wheels: This Month's Road Test"

8. the fashion articles

9. the food and health articles, plus "Finding and Choosing Your Own Doctor"

10.–11. *Answers will vary.*

Ask Anna

1. the ex-boyfriend
2. the girlfriend, if he thinks she's being sincere
3. Talk to parents when everyone's relaxed; discuss issue, ask for more responsibility; ask for ways to demonstrate responsibility and trustworthiness.
4. hiking, biking, swimming, aerobics
5. feel better physically, improved coordination and self-image
6. can't, in school phys ed classes
7.–10. *Answers will vary.*

Monthly Horoscope

1. (a) Capricorn
   (b) Libra
   (c) Aries
   (d) Pisces
   (e) Cancer
   (f) Virgo
2. (a) Gemini
   (b) Sagittarius

   (c) Cancer
   (d) Scorpio
   (e) Leo
   (f) Aquarius
   (g) Taurus
   (h) Virgo
3. *Answers will vary.*

Weather Forecast

1. (a) Saturday
   (b) Thursday morning
   (c) Wednesday night
   (d) Thursday afternoon
   (e) Sunday
   (f) Saturday
   (g) Thursday afternoon

   (h) Wednesday morning
   (i) Wednesday night
2. Sunday
3. Friday
4. around 5:30 to 6:00 A.M. or 6:00 P.M.
5.–6. *Answers will vary.*

How Well Do You Cope with Stress?

Answers will vary.

UNIT 1. AROUND THE HOUSE

You use many products around the house. Each one is different, and each one has to be used differently. Even your clothes can't all be treated alike. So you need to be able to read the instructions for use and care that come with each item. Practice this kind of reading here. First, get to know some of the vocabulary words in this section. Write the correct word from the following list on the blank next to its definition below.

adequate	extinguisher	inhale	physician
contaminate	flush	interval	residue
discharge	hazardous	irritation	vapor
disinfect	incinerate	maintenance	ventilation

_____ 1. Dangerous

_____ 2. To make impure or harmful by contact with something unclean or unsafe

_____ 3. Soreness, swelling, roughness, redness

_____ 4. Circulation or flow of air

_____ 5. To burn

_____ 6. To breathe in

_____ 7. Doctor

_____ 8. To clean; to free from infection

_____ 9. To wash out with a flow of water

_____ 10. A device that puts out a flame or light

_____ 11. Keeping something in good condition or operation

_____ 12. A space of time between events; a pause

_____ 13. Something that remains

_____ 14. To fire off; to release; to pour the contents out

_____ 15. Gas; matter suspended in the air, like smoke or fog

_____ 16. Enough

ALL-PURPOSE CLEANER

Cleans and shines washable household surfaces. Removes grease, soap scum, grime, most stains, and dirt.

> ### Kitchen
> Countertops, sinks, cabinets, appliances, floors

> ### Bathroom
> Sinks, tubs, tiles, toilets, showers, floors

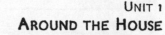

Directions for Use

Easy to Use. Just spray on and wipe off. No scrubbing or rinsing required. Safe for most kitchen and bathroom surfaces. Contains no harsh abrasives or acids. Use on washable surfaces such as fiberglass, porcelain, stainless steel, synthetic marble, tile, plastic, and vinyl. For other surfaces, spot test in an inconspicuous area.

It is a violation of federal law to use this product in a manner inconsistent with its labeling.

- **To clean:** Point nozzle toward surface to be cleaned. Spray 6–8 inches from dirty surface until thoroughly wet. Wipe off with clean lint-free cloth, paper towel, or sponge. For stubborn stains, allow 15–20 seconds before wiping.

- **To disinfect:** (nonporous surfaces) Clean first, then spray on surface until thoroughly wet. Let stand for 10 minutes. Wipe with damp cloth, paper towel, or sponge.

- **To control mold and mildew:** Spray on surface until thoroughly wet. Leave 3 minutes. Wipe with damp cloth, paper towel, or sponge.

Caution

Hazardous to humans and domestic animals.

- May cause eye irritation. Avoid contact with eyes or skin. In case of eye contact, flush eyes with water for 15 minutes.

- In case of skin contact, wash immediately and thoroughly with soap and water. Consult a physician if irritation occurs.

- **Keep out of reach of children.**

- Do not mix with other household cleaners.

- **Storage/Disposal:** Store in original container in areas inaccessible to small children. Do not reuse empty container. Rinse empty container thoroughly and discard in trash.

ALL-PURPOSE CLEANER

1. Name two advantages of using this product, according to the label.

   (a) _____

   (b) _____

2. List four things in a bathroom you could use this product on.

   (a) _____

   (b) _____

   (c) _____

   (d) _____

3. What are the first two steps you would follow to clean the bathroom tiles?

   _____

4. What two bathroom problems does this product control?

   (a) _____

   (b) _____

5. How long do you leave this product on a surface if you are:

   (a) cleaning normal dirt and soap scum? _____

   (b) cleaning stubborn stains? _____

   (c) disinfecting a surface? _____

   (d) controlling mold, mildew? _____

6. Suppose you spray some of this product on your skin. What should you do?

   _____

   _____

(continued)

ALL-PURPOSE CLEANER (CONTINUED)

What Do You Think?

7. The label says to store this product in the original container. Give two reasons why this might be a good idea.

   _____

   _____

8. You are supposed to keep this product out of children's reach. What does this mean? How could you do this?

   _____

   _____

9. The label says you can use this cleaner on washable surfaces such as the following ones. Give an example of each, if possible, in your own home:

   (a) fiberglass _____

   (b) porcelain _____

   (c) stainless steel _____

   (d) synthetic marble _____

   (e) tile _____

   (f) plastic _____

   (g) vinyl _____

10. The directions say, Do not mix with other household cleaners. Why? What might happen if you mix together two or more household cleaners?

    _____

    _____

    _____

Parka

Size: Large
Shell: 85% Wool/15% Nylon
Lining: 100% Nylon
Fill: 100% Polyester
Machine wash cool. Non-chlorine bleach if needed. Line dry. Do not iron.

Blouse

All Nylon Antron III exclusive of decoration or overlay
Machine wash warm.
Wash dark colors separately.
No bleach. Tumble dry low heat.
Cool iron.

Sweater

70% Wool/30% Polyester
Turn garment inside out.
Machine wash medium or hand wash warm. Do not bleach. Tumble dry low heat. Lay flat to dry.

Robe

Size: M
100% Pure Silk
Hand wash separately in cold water.
Do not bleach. Line dry. Iron damp, warm setting.
Dry cleaning recommended.

Tank Top

100% Cotton
Machine wash cold delicate cycle. Do not bleach. Tumble dry low. Cool iron if necessary.

Suit Jacket

65% Polyester/35% Cotton
For best results, hand wash in cool water or machine wash gentle cycle in cool water. Do not bleach. Do not wring. Lay flat to dry or tumble dry at low setting or professionally dry clean.

Sweatshirt

100% Cotton
Machine wash warm with like colors.
Non-chlorine bleach when needed.
Tumble dry medium. Do not iron if decorated.

CLOTHING LABELS

A. Put a check (✓) by each statement that follows the directions on the care and content label for each item of clothing. Then cross out the statements that don't follow the directions.

1. Sweater

   _____ (a) Hang on line to dry.

   _____ (b) Use non-chlorine bleach.

   _____ (c) Wash in warm water.

   _____ (d) Wash inside out.

2. Tank top

   _____ (a) Don't use any bleach.

   _____ (b) Wash on regular cycle in cool water.

   _____ (c) Remove wrinkles with warm iron.

   _____ (d) Dry in clothes dryer at low temperature.

3. Parka

   _____ (a) Hang on line to dry.

   _____ (b) Iron on cool setting.

   _____ (c) Use non-chlorine bleach.

   _____ (d) Wash in cool water.

4. Sweatshirt

   _____ (a) Use non-chlorine bleach.

   _____ (b) Dry in clothes dryer at medium temperature.

   _____ (c) Always iron.

   _____ (d) Wash with clothes of about the same color.

(continued)

6

Essential Everyday Reading

CLOTHING LABELS *(CONTINUED)*

B. Tell which items of clothing can be washed in the following ways.

5. Machine wash cool—no bleach

_____   _____

6. Machine wash warm—no bleach

_____   _____

7. Hand wash only

_____   _____

8. Hand wash or machine wash

_____   _____

9. Which items can you iron?

_____   _____

10. Which items can you dry in the clothes dryer?

_____   _____

What Do You Think?

11. What could happen to the different items of clothing if you didn't follow the care and content labels?

_____

_____

_____

_____

_____

[A small fire has started in your laundry room. You have to put it out right away!]

Instructions

1. Pull pin. Hold unit upright.

2. Aim at base of fire. Stand back 6 feet.

3. Squeeze lever and sweep from side to side.

Do not test. Any use requires recharging.

Maintenance

Follow instructions on nameplate and in owner's manual. If owner's manual is lost, immediately contact manufacturer for replacement. Inspect monthly or at more frequent intervals if exposed to weather or vandalism. Check pressure gauge—if below operating range, extinguisher is not in a ready-to-use condition and requires immediate servicing. Examine nozzle for obstructions. Check that ring pull pin is intact. Extinguisher to be installed, inspected, maintained, and tested in accordance with the Standards of the National Fire Protection Association titled Portable Fire Extinguishers. Meets DOT requirements for aluminum cylinders.

Caution

- Do not incinerate. Contents under pressure.

- Do not expose to temperatures over 120°F (48°C). Operable temperature range –40°F to 120°F (–40°C [sic] to 48°C).

- Do not aim at a person's face.

- Keep away from children.

- After use, immediately clean all surfaces contacted by dry chemical agent.

First Aid

Flush eyes with clean, cool water. Wash exposed skin areas thoroughly. Seek fresh air and contact physician immediately.

Warning

Improper use of this cylinder could cause serious bodily injury or property damage.

Recharge

Recharge immediately after any use. Extinguisher must be recharged only by a qualified fire extinguisher service company. Failure to comply with these instructions may cause property damage, bodily injury, or both. Completely discharge unit before removing valve.

FIRE EXTINGUISHER

1. What should you do if you lose the owner's manual?

   _____

   _____

2. Why should you **not** test the fire extinguisher?

   _____

   _____

   _____

3. Since you can't test the fire extinguisher, how can you tell if it's ready to use?

   _____

   _____

   _____

4. List four things you need to do regularly to be sure the fire extinguisher is always ready to use.

   (a) _____

   (b) _____

   (c) _____

   (d) _____

5. Number these steps in the correct order for using the fire extinguisher.

   _____ Aim the spray at the base of the fire.

   _____ Sweep spray from side to side.

   _____ Squeeze lever.

   _____ Pull pin.

(continued)

FIRE EXTINGUISHER *(CONTINUED)*

6. Describe how you would flush your eyes if you got some of the fire extinguisher chemical in them.

_____

_____

_____

_____

7. What should you do with the fire extinguisher after you have used it?

_____

_____

_____

_____

What Do You Think?

8. The directions say, "Keep away from children." Why?

_____

_____

_____

_____

9. The directions also say to contact a physician if you get fire extinguisher chemical in your eyes or on your skin. How would you do this?

_____

_____

_____

_____

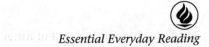

- Kills insect pests on contact
- Leaves a residue that keeps on killing insects
- Vapor penetrates cracks and crevices to kill hidden bugs.

Directions For Use

- **Spray on surfaces only:** Do not spray into the air. Hold container about 12 inches from surface to be sprayed. Be sure to point valve opening toward the surface being sprayed. Push button and spray until the surface is thoroughly wet.

- **To kill cockroaches:** Spray cracks and baseboards until wet; spray any scurrying bugs directly. Repeat as needed.

- **To kill ants:** Spray ant trails and around entry points such as doors and windows. Repeat as needed.

- **To kill other crawling insects:** Spray infested areas and repeat as needed.

Precautionary Statements: Hazardous to humans and domestic animals

Warning

Harmful if swallowed or inhaled. If swallowed, get immediate medical attention. Do not get on skin, eyes, or clothing. Wash hands thoroughly with soap and water immediately after using. Remove children and pets from area before spraying, and keep away until treated areas are dry.

Use with adequate ventilation. Avoid breathing spray. Do not spray for longer than one minute in a room. Do not spray humans or pets. Avoid contaminating food, utensils, dishes, or food preparation areas. Do not smoke when using. Do not spray plants or shrubs.

Caution

Do not use near fire or flame.

ROACH AND ANT KILLER

1. What kinds of insect pests can you control with this product?

   _____

   _____

   _____

2. Name the areas you would spray to control:

   (a) cockroaches _____

   (b) ants _____

   (c) other crawling insects _____

3. Name five things in a home that you should **not** spray:

   (a) _____

   (b) _____

   (c) _____

   (d) _____

   (e) _____

4. What must you do before you spray?

   _____

   _____

   _____

5. What must you do after you spray?

   _____

   _____

   _____

(continued)

ROACH AND ANT KILLER *(CONTINUED)*

6. Suppose your little brother sprays some of this product into his mouth. What would you do?

_____

_____

_____

What Do You Think?

7. The directions say to avoid breathing the spray. How would you do this?

_____

_____

_____

_____

_____

8. What might happen if you used this product near a burning candle?

_____

_____

_____

_____

9. Would you use this product to control flying insects? Why or why not?

_____

_____

_____

_____

Name _____

Date _____

UNIT 2. AUTOMOTIVE

Many times when you pump gas, you have to follow the directions at the pump. Your owner's manual tells you how to change a tire so you don't have to call a tow truck. When your car needs service, you have to read the repair shop's signs and bills.

Practice this kind of reading here. First, get to know some of the vocabulary words in this section. Write the correct word from the following list on the blank next to its definition below.

authorize	credit	install	rotate
bay	engage	negligence	signature
chassis	fee	nozzle	specify
compartment	groove	receipt	vehicle

_____ 1. Short tube on the end of a hose

_____ 2. Something written that says goods or money have been received

_____ 3. To give someone authority or legal power to do something

_____ 4. Frame of a car

_____ 5. To name or state in detail

_____ 6. Name of a person written in his or her own hand

_____ 7. To cause mechanical parts to mesh or activate

_____ 8. Section of enclosed space

_____ 9. Something that carries or transports something else

_____ 10. Enclosed space in a building for a car to go into

_____ 11. Careless action

_____ 12. A charge for services

_____ 13. To build in

_____ 14. To turn around

_____ 15. Time allowed for payment

_____ 16. Slot; long, narrow channel

GAS PUMP

[It's pouring rain, you don't have a jacket, and there's no roof over the gas pumps. You want to pump this gas fast!]

Price per gallon including taxes:

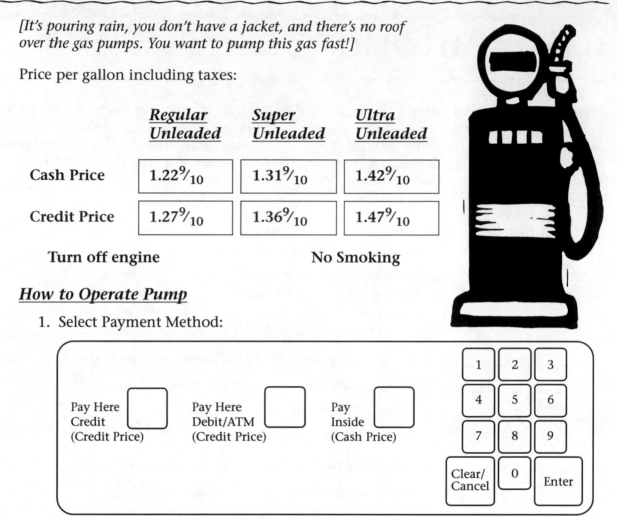

	Regular Unleaded	*Super Unleaded*	*Ultra Unleaded*
Cash Price	$1.22^9/_{10}$	$1.31^9/_{10}$	$1.42^9/_{10}$
Credit Price	$1.27^9/_{10}$	$1.36^9/_{10}$	$1.47^9/_{10}$

Turn off engine   **No Smoking**

How to Operate Pump

1. Select Payment Method:

Pay Here Credit (Credit Price) ☐   Pay Here Debit/ATM (Credit Price) ☐   Pay Inside (Cash Price) ☐

1	2	3
4	5	6
7	8	9
Clear/Cancel	0	Enter

2. Select grade by removing nozzle, place in fuel tank.

3. Lift hook ON, wait until computer resets to zero.

4. Operate nozzle for fuel delivery.

5. After completing delivery, lower hook OFF.

6. Replace nozzle.

7. Wait for receipt or pay inside.

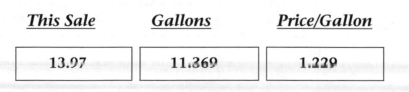

This Sale	*Gallons*	*Price/Gallon*
13.97	11.369	1.229

Essential Everyday Reading

GAS PUMP

1. Which type of gas is cheapest? _____

   Which costs the most? _____

2. What is the first thing you should do at the gas pump, according to the directions?

   _____

3. What would you use the numbered keypad for? _____

   _____

   What would you do if you made a mistake punching numbers into the keypad?

   _____

4. Number these steps in the correct order for pumping gas.

   _____ Pump gas into fuel tank through nozzle.

   _____ Replace nozzle.

   _____ Lift hook on nozzle rest to "On" position.

   _____ Select your payment method.

   _____ Take your receipt.

   _____ Wait until computer resets to zero.

   _____ Lower hook on nozzle rest to "Off" position.

   _____ Place nozzle of the fuel grade you want in the fuel tank.

5. How would you pay for the gas if you chose to pay cash?

   _____

   _____

(continued)

GAS PUMP *(CONTINUED)*

6. How would you pay for the gas if you chose "Pay Here Credit"?

   _____

   _____

7. How would you pay for the gas if you chose "Pay Here Debit/ATM"?

   _____

   _____

What Do You Think?

8. What would be the advantages of paying for gas by credit? the disadvantages?

   _____

   _____

   _____

   _____

   _____

9. Which kind of gas would you choose for your car? Why? What does your car's owner's manual recommend?

   _____

   _____

   _____

   _____

   _____

   _____

Parts

Qty.	Part #/Description	Amount
4	Spark plugs	14.00
1	Rotor	6.30
1	Fuel filter	18.96
1	Belt	11.28
	Total Parts	**$50.54**

Oil, Grease, Fluids

4 qts	Oil	11.96
	Total	**$62.50**

Description	Labor Charge	Description	Labor Charge
Change Oil	$6.00	State Inspection	6.00
Change Oil Filter	3.00	Repair Shocks	
Chassis Lube	3.00	Brake Check	
Rotate Tires	7.50	Brake Repair	
Emission		Transmission	
Balance Tires	12.50	Front End Align.	
Repair Wiper Blades	17.50	Engine Tune-up	42.00
Adjust Clutch		Cooling System	
Service Auto. Trans.		Other (Specify)	12.50
A/C		**Total Labor**	**$110.00**
Repair Exhaust		**Tax**	**$3.13**
		Pay This Amount	**$175.63**

I hereby authorize the above repair work to be done along with necessary materials. You and the employees may operate above vehicle for purposes of testing, inspection, or delivery at my risk. It is understood that you will not be held responsible for loss or damage to vehicles or articles left in vehicles due to fire or theft.

_____
(*Signature*)

AUTO REPAIR

1. Write **True** or **False** for each statement below.

   _____ (a) Spark plugs cost $14 each.

   _____ (b) Repair shop changed your oil.

   _____ (c) Cost of parts installed in your car is $11.96 (before tax).

   _____ (d) Cost of oil is $2.99 per quart (before tax).

   _____ (e) Repair shop did a state inspection of your car.

   _____ (f) Exhaust system has been repaired.

   _____ (g) Repair shop is at fault if tape deck is stolen from your car while in shop.

   _____ (h) Altogether, work on your tires cost $20 (before tax).

   _____ (i) Charge for amount of time mechanic worked on your car is $100 (before tax).

   _____ (j) Only you may drive your car.

2. What has the repair shop left out on the line titled "Other"?

   _____

   _____

What Do You Think?

3. What do these abbreviations stand for?

   Qty. _____   Lube _____

   No. _____   A/C _____

   Auto. Trans. _____   Align. _____

4. How can you be sure you are being charged fairly for an auto repair and that all the repairs really needed to be done?

   _____

   _____

Notice to Our Customers
Required Under State Law

Before we begin making repairs, you have a right to put in writing the total amount you agree to pay for repairs. You will not have to pay anything over that amount unless you agree to it when we contact you later.

Before you pay your bill, you have a right to inspect any replaced parts. You have a right to take with you any replaced parts, unless we are required to return the parts to our distributor or manufacturer.

We cannot install any used or rebuilt parts unless you specifically agree in advance.

You cannot be charged any fee for exercising these rights.

We charge $42 per hour for labor.

We round off to the nearest tenth. We may also charge for our repair services either by the flat or "menu price" method. Ask our service advisor to explain what method will be used in charging you and to show you how much it will cost you.

AUTO SERVICE NOTICE

1. Put a check (✓) next to each case below in which the repair shop has followed its policy as stated in the Notice to Customers.

   _____ (a) You agreed in writing to pay $150 for repairs. The shop has billed you $200, and says you have to pay before you can get your car back.

   _____ (b) The shop replaced a shock absorber and had to send the bad shock back to the manufacturer, even though you also wanted it back.

   _____ (c) The cost of a part was $12.5993. The shop billed you $12.60.

   _____ (d) The shop billed you $96 for labor for a one-hour repair job.

   _____ (e) The shop kept your old water pump so they could rebuild and resell it, even though you wanted it back.

   _____ (f) The shop charged you $10 extra to take your old starter home with you.

   _____ (g) The shop billed you $21.00 for labor for a half-hour repair job.

   _____ (h) The shop installed a used, rebuilt radiator in your car without asking you if this was okay.

2. The shop charges you $69.96 for a tune-up, including parts. Is this an example of flat or menu pricing?

   _____

   _____

3. The shop charges you for four quarts of oil at $2.99 per quart, for an oil filter, and for an air filter, and also charges you for the time spent changing the oil and installing the filters. Is this an example of flat or menu pricing?

   _____

   _____

(continued)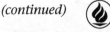

AUTO SERVICE NOTICE *(CONTINUED)*

What Do You Think?

4. Why do you think customers have a right to see and take with them any replacement parts?

_____

_____

_____

_____

_____

5. Would you ever agree to have used or rebuilt parts installed in your car? Why or why not? under what circumstances?

_____

_____

_____

_____

_____

_____

Caution!

Before you begin:

- Pull your car a safe distance off the road, so neither you nor your vehicle are in the path of oncoming traffic.

- Be sure your car is on firm, solid, level ground.

- Turn on emergency flashers.

- Set your parking brake. Block the wheels on the other side of the car from the flat tire.

- Have all passengers get out of your vehicle.

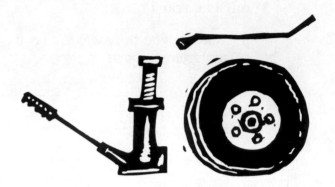

How to Change a Flat Tire

1. Take spare tire, jack, and lug wrench out of the luggage compartment.

2. Remove hubcap from wheel and place in luggage compartment.

3. Loosen wheel nuts with lug wrench, about one turn counterclockwise.

4. Find the jack points on the side of the car under the body. They are marked by a groove. Guide the lifting bracket of the jack so it is directly under this groove. Be sure the jack is on firm ground. Place a board under the jack to make the ground firm if necessary.

5. With the jack base firmly on the ground, turn the jack handle clockwise. Raise the vehicle just enough to put the spare tire on.

6. Now, unscrew the wheel nuts fully and remove the wheel with the flat tire. Put the spare wheel on the wheel hub so the threaded bolts go through the holes in the wheel. Screw the wheel nuts back onto the bolts, tightening them by hand in a crisscross pattern.

7. Turn the jack handle counterclockwise to lower the vehicle until the spare tire touches the ground.

8. Tighten the wheel nuts firmly in a crisscross pattern using the lug wrench.

9. Lower the vehicle fully and remove the jack.

10. Place damaged tire, jack, and lug wrench in spare tire storage space.

Be sure to have the damaged road tire repaired and reinstalled promptly, along with its wheel rim and the hubcap.

TIRE CHANGING

1. Explain how you would block the wheels while changing a tire.

   _____

   _____

   _____

2. Show in a sketch how you
   would turn something
   Clockwise: Counterclockwise:

3. Put a check (✓) next to each of the following situations in which the person is acting safely while changing a tire. For those who are acting dangerously, tell what that person is doing wrong and what he or she should do instead.

_____ (a) Lanie pulls her car safely off the road onto the soft sand shoulder.

   _____

   _____

_____ (b) Deon tightens the wheel nuts firmly after the spare tire is on the ground.

   _____

   _____

_____ (c) Ramon places the jack under what looks like the strongest part of the car.

   _____

   _____

_____ (d) Vanessa turns her emergency flashers on.

   _____

   _____

(continued)

TIRE CHANGING (CONTINUED)

_____ (e) Beatriz removes the wheel nuts and then jacks up the car.

_____

_____

_____ (f) Bob raises the car as high as the jack will go.

_____

_____

What Do You Think?

4. Find each of these in your car. Draw a small sketch of each, and tell what it is used for.

(a) spare tire _____   (d) hubcap _____

_____   _____

(b) wheel nuts _____   (e) wheel bolts _____

_____   _____

(c) lug wrench _____   (f) jack _____

_____   _____

5. Supervised by someone who is experienced in changing tires, practice changing the tire on your car if you have never done this before. Follow the directions in your car's owner's manual, and be sure to follow all safety cautions.

[You've never been through a car wash before. Now it's your turn. You don't want the friends in the car with you to think you don't know what you're doing. You want to follow all the directions, but you need to read them quickly!]

Before Entering Wash:

- Remove/lower antennas.
- Fold in mirrors on vans.
- Close windows.

To Operate Car Wash:

- Enter code on keypad.
- Drive slowly into bay.
- Stop vehicle when front wheel drops into bay plate and red light comes on.
- Put vehicle in park/neutral.
- Engage emergency brake.
- Exit slowly when light comes on.

Do Not Wash:

- All-terrain vehicles
- Vehicles with loose items in pickup bed
- Vehicles with body damage, loose chrome or nonstandard accessories
- Vehicles with exposed propane or compressed gas tanks

Not Responsible for:

- Antennas
- Mirrors/loose chrome
- Damage due to driver's negligence
- Clearcoat finishes
- Polyglycol seal finishes

Car Wash Menu

The Works $6

- Wash, Foam Bath, Undercarriage, Wheel Scrub, Hot Wax, Dry

Premium $5

- Wash, Foam Bath, Undercarriage, Wax, Dry

Deluxe $4

- Wash, Wax, Dry

Express $3

- Wash

Save $1 on any wash with fill-up of gasoline (8 gal min.)

CAR WASH

1. Name four things that the instructions suggest could be damaged by the car wash.

   (a) _____

   (b) _____

   (c) _____

   (d) _____

2. If you choose The Works for $6, what extras do you get that you don't get with Deluxe for $4?

   _____

   _____

3. Put a check (✓) next to the things you **should** do when going through the car wash. Cross out the things you should **not** do.

   _____ (a) Drive through in low gear.

   _____ (b) Put your emergency brake on.

   _____ (c) Close your windows.

   _____ (d) Leave antenna up.

   _____ (e) Tie down or remove items in pickup truck bed.

   _____ (f) Take your all-terrain vehicle through.

   _____ (g) Exit quickly when you see the red light.

4. What kind of vehicle might have "exposed propane or compressed gas tanks"? Why?

   _____

   _____

(continued)

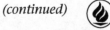

CAR WASH (CONTINUED)

5. How can you get a car washed for $1 less than the menu price?

_____

_____

_____

6. Whose fault is it if the mirror on your van is damaged in the car wash?

_____

_____

_____

What Do You Think?

7. Give an example of a "nonstandard accessory" that should not be washed.

_____

_____

_____

8. The Works and Premium wash the undercarriage. What is the undercarriage? Why might it be good to wash the undercarriage?

_____

_____

_____

9. Would you take your car through a car wash? Why or why not?

_____

_____

_____

Unit 3. Banking and Finance

We all need money. To get your money in and out of your bank accounts, you have to read bank and store forms and instructions. Practice this kind of reading here. First, get to know some of the vocabulary words in this section. Write the correct word from the following list on the blank next to the word's definition below.

account	deposit	loan	varies
application	express	minimum	verification
balance	identification	transaction	waive
checkout	interest	transferred	withdrawal

_____ 1. Money placed in a bank account

_____ 2. Money given for temporary use, to be repaid with interest

_____ 3. A sum of money, belonging to a person, in a bank

_____ 4. Establishing the truth or accuracy of something

_____ 5. Money taken out of a bank account

_____ 6. Moved from one place to another

_____ 7. The counter where store purchases are added up and paid for

_____ 8. Form used to apply for something

_____ 9. Least amount possible or allowed

_____ 10. Evidence showing who you are

_____ 11. Fast, quick

_____ 12. A business act

_____ 13. Amount in a bank account

_____ 14. To give up or not enforce a right

_____ 15. Amount earned on money deposited in a bank; amount paid for borrowed money

_____ 16. Changes; does not stay the same

Bank–Express Payment Envelope

Deposit or Loan Payment Envelope Instructions:

1. Use a separate envelope for each deposit or loan payment.

2. Make sure you've filled in all necessary information.

3. Place check or cash into envelope. No coins, please.

4. No deposit slip is necessary, other than this envelope.

Name _____   Daytime Telephone _____
         (Please print)

Type of Account or Loan   No more than 25 bills to be enclosed.
(Check one)   No coins.

___ Savings   Cash $_____
___ Checking   Checks $_____
___ Money Market $_____
___ Loan Payment $_____
___ Credit Line $_____
                                          Total Enclosed $_____

Deposits made after 3 P.M. on a business day and all loan payments will be credited the next business day. All deposits are subject to verification.

Withdrawal Form

Name _____ $ _____

Amount _____ Dollars
              (In words)

Account # _____   Date _____

Signature _____

I want this withdrawal in:

___ Cash _____

___ A Bank Check # _____

___ Transferred to Account # _____

New Address? Please tell us.

BANK FORMS

1. What can you use this envelope for? _____

   _____

   _____

   _____

2. What kinds of accounts can you make a deposit into when you use this envelope?

   (a) _____

   (b) _____

   (c) _____

3. What kinds of payments can you make when you use this envelope?

   (a) _____

   (b) _____

4. What **can** you put in the envelope?

   (a) _____

   (b) _____

5. What **can't** you put in the envelope to make a deposit or payment?

   (a) _____

   (b) _____

6. Do you need to fill out a separate deposit slip? _____

   _____

(continued)

BANK FORMS (CONTINUED)

7. If you make a deposit at 4 P.M. on Wednesday, when will the deposit be added to your account?

_____

_____

_____

8. Your loan payment is due October 1. You make the payment in this envelope on October 1. Is your payment on time? Why or why not?

_____

_____

_____

_____

9. You can take a withdrawal in three different ways. What are they?

(a) _____

(b) _____

(c) _____

What Do You Think?

10. Why might you use an express payment envelope instead of going to a window and giving your deposit to a bank teller?

_____

_____

_____

_____

_____

CHECK-CASHING POLICY AND PROCEDURES

At the Checkouts

1. We accept personal checks only at the checkout.

2. Our check-cashing card or pre-approval at the service desk is required for paying by check through the checkout.

3. After completion of a check-cashing application, we will preapprove one check in a seven-day period until the check-cashing card is received.

4. We will accept checks for $30 over the amount of purchase with our check-cashing card.

At the Service Desk

1. Our check-cashing card is required for all check cashing privileges at the service desk.

2. We will cash up to two personal checks per seven-day period for amounts up to $75 each. The minimum amount is $5.

3. We will cash one payroll check per seven-day period for up to $500. We will require two additional pieces of identification for checks over $300.

4. We will cash one government check per seven-day period for up to $600. We will require two additional pieces of identification for checks over $300.

5. There will be a charge of 50¢ for each check cashed at the service desk.

6. We will not cash two-party checks, and we reserve the right to refuse any check at any time.

We will impose a $15 handling fee on each check returned unpaid by your bank.

CHECK-CASHING POLICY AND PROCEDURES

1. For each of the checks listed below, tell in each column what you need to cash it.

	Cash at checkout or service desk	What kind of ID do you need?
(a) A government check for $500		
(b) A personal check for $35		
(c) A check for your groceries plus $20		
(d) A payroll check for $230		
(e) A government check for $295		
(f) A payroll check for $345		

2. Which of these checks will be accepted at the checkout?

_____ (a) A personal check without a check-cashing card but preapproved at the service desk

_____ (b) A personal check for $30 for cash and no groceries

3. Which of these checks will be accepted at the service desk with a check-cashing card?

_____ (a) A check made out to your brother that he has signed over to you

_____ (b) A personal check for $4

_____ (c) A second paycheck on Wednesday after you cashed one a week ago Monday

_____ (d) A personal check for $30 on Monday and another personal check for $45 on Friday

(continued)

CHECK-CASHING POLICY AND PROCEDURES *(CONTINUED)*

4. What is a "check returned unpaid by your bank"?

_____

_____

_____

_____

_____

What Do You Think?

5. Do you think it's fair to charge 50¢ for each check cashed at the service desk? Why or why not?

_____

_____

_____

_____

6. If you need to show "two additional pieces of identification," what could you show?

_____

_____

_____

Checking Accounts

Basic Checking
- Minimum to open: $25.
- Service charge: $3 a month.
  Fee covers 16 transactions per month. You will be
  charged an additional 25¢ for each transaction over 16.
- Minimum balance: None.

> For customers over age 60, no service fee or extra transaction fees are charged, and no minimum balances are required.

Personal Checking
- Minimum to open: $50.
- Service charge: None, if you maintain a $300 minimum balance in your
  account; if your balance falls below $300, you will be charged a $6 monthly fee
  plus an additional 25¢ for each transaction over 16.

NOW (Interest) Checking
- Minimum to open: $50.
- Service charge: None, if you maintain a $500 minimum balance in your
  account; if your balance falls below $500, you will be charged a $6 monthly fee
  plus an additional 25¢ for each transaction over 20.
- Interest rate: Varies; paid on average monthly balance.

Savings Accounts

Passbook Savings
- Minimum to open: $50 ($10 for minors).
- Monthly fee: None, for balances of $100 or more; $1 for balances under $100;
  waived for minors and customers age 60 and over.
- Minimum to earn interest: $25 balance.
- Interest rate: Varies; see current schedule.
- All transactions are posted in your passbook as they occur.

Statement Savings
- Minimum to open: $25 (minors $10).
- Monthly fee: None, for balances of $50 or more; $1 for balances under $50;
  waived for minors and customers age 60 and over.
- Minimum to earn interest: None.
- Interest rate: Varies; see current schedule.
- Monthly statement shows all of month's transactions, interest earned,
  current balance.

Holiday Club Accounts
- Minimum to open: $5.
- Interest paid on clubs completed. No interest paid on clubs closed prior to
  maturity. Bonus paid when you complete the club.
- Withdrawal prior to maturity: $1 fee.

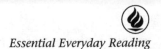

CHECKING AND SAVINGS ACCOUNTS

1. Read each of the following features. Then put an X in the column or columns of the checking account with that feature.

	Basic	Personal	NOW
(a) Earns interest			
(b) Minimum to open is $50			
(c) Minimum to open is $50			
(d) Monthly service charge is $3			
(e) No service charge if minimum balance is $500			
(f) 25¢ transaction fee			
(g) No service charge if minimum balance is $300			
(h) May have a monthly service charge of $6			
(i) Minimum to open is $25			
(j) 25¢ transaction fee over 16 transactions per month			
(k) No minimum balance			
(l) 25¢ transaction fee over 20 transactions per month			

(continued)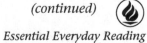

CHECKING AND SAVINGS ACCOUNTS (CONTINUED)

2. Read each of the following features. Then put an X in the column or columns of the savings account with that feature

	Passbook	Statement	Holiday
(a) Minimum to open is $5			
(b) Monthly fee $0 for balance of $100 or more			
(c) Monthly fee $1 for balance under $50			
(d) No interest on account closed early			
(e) Interest on any balance over zero			
(f) Interest on balance of $25 or more			
(g) Balance is shown in passbook			
(h) Monthly fee of $1 for balance under $100			
(i) No monthly fee for balance of $50 or more			
(j) Bonus on accounts held to maturity			

What Do You Think?

3. Which would you choose, a checking or a savings account? Why?

_____

_____

_____

_____

4. Would you consider opening a Holiday Club account? Why or why not? What is the disadvantage of this type of club?

_____

_____

_____

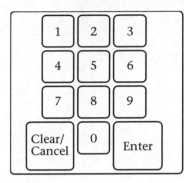

[People are waiting behind you to use the automated teller machine. They seem very impatient. You want to finish using the machine quickly!]

(Screen 1)

Welcome to Finance City Bank
Your Banking Center
Please Insert Your ATM Card
for Instant Service

(Screen 2)

Enter Your Personal ID No. (PIN)
Press Here When Done ☐
Press Cancel If Error Made

(Screen 3)

Notice to User
Your financial institution may assess
a fee for any transaction you process
through this machine.
Please contact your financial
institution for further information.

(Screen 4)

Select Your Transaction
Press Cancel If Error Made

Withdrawal _____ ☐
Deposit _____ ☐
Transfer _____ ☐
Balance Inquiry _____ ☐

(Screen 5)

Select Type of Withdrawal

Press Cancel If Error Made

From Checking _____ ☐
From Savings _____ ☐
From Credit Card _____ ☐

(Screen 6)

Enter Whole Dollar Amount
in Multiples of $5.00
$ 0.00

Press If Correct _____ ☐
Press If Incorrect _____ ☐

(Screen 7)

Transfer Being Processed
Please Wait

(Screen 8)

Take Cash Below

(Screen 9)

Transfer Completed
Please Take Your Card and Record

ATM DIRECTIONS

1. How do you start the machine? _____

_____

2. How do you find out how much money you have in your account?

_____

_____

_____

3. If you want to withdraw $20 from your checking account, what do you enter at screens 4, 5, and 6?

    (a) Screen 4: _____

    (b) Screen 5: _____

    (c) Screen 6: _____

4. Do you have to pay a fee for using your ATM card? _____

    Which screen tells you this? _____

5. Do you get a written record of your ATM transaction? _____

    Which screen tells you this? _____

6. If you want to deposit $15 into your savings account, what do you enter at screens 4, 5, and 6?

    (a) Screen 4: _____

    (b) Screen 5: _____

    (c) Screen 6: _____

(continued)

ATM DIRECTIONS *(CONTINUED)*

7. After inserting your ATM card, what must you do to move on to screens 3 and 4?

   _____

   _____

   How do you do this? _____

   _____

8. Could you withdraw $18 or deposit $7? _____

   Which screen tells you this? _____

9. What do you do if you make a mistake (press the wrong button) while you are entering information into the machine?

   _____

   _____

What Do You Think?

10. What does ATM stand for? _____

11. What is a cardholder's Personal ID No.?

    _____

    _____

    _____

    Why do you think the machine asks for this?

    _____

    _____

    _____

Name _____

Date _____

Unit 4. Out in Public

You'll find lots of signs and directions when you're out in public. When can you visit people in the hospital? How do you run the machines at the self-service laundry? How do you use a pay phone, ride a bus, sign into a campground, or use the computer at the library? Read the signs and directions. Practice this kind of reading here. First, get to know some of the vocabulary words in this section. Write the correct word from the following list on the blank next to the word's definition below.

confirmation   emergency   maximum   scroll
conversation   fabric   prohibited sibling
detergent   fare   register   smolder
dial   flammable   resume   terminal

_____ 1. To operate a telephone

_____ 2. Able to catch on fire easily and burn very quickly

_____ 3. Substance used for cleaning

_____ 4. Cloth, or material that resembles cloth

_____ 5. Amount paid for transportation—for instance, to ride a bus

_____ 6. Forbidden; not allowed

_____ 7. To enroll or sign into a place

_____ 8. Assuring that something is so; proof

_____ 9. Greatest amount possible or allowed

_____ 10. Brother or sister

_____ 11. To burn slowly

_____ 12. Talk, discussion

_____ 13. Device that lets you communicate with a computer

_____ 14. To move up and down through a computer file

_____ 15. To start again

_____ 16. Unexpected situation that calls for immediate action

[It's rush hour. Lots of cranky people are pushing onto the bus behind you. You want to pay quickly so you can get one of the last empty seats.]

Deposit Exact Fare

Drivers do not make change.

Full fare $1.15 or 1 token
No dollar bills

- Senior citizens   50¢
  Have Medicare or Metro ID
  card visible for driver
- Disabled persons   50¢
- Students   50¢
- Children under 5 years   Free
  (Limit 2 with adult)
- Transfers   Free
All others pay full fare.

Notice

Bureau regulations require passengers to stand behind white line.

Driver cannot engage in unnecessary conversation.

Spitting, smoking, or the carrying of smoldering cigars, cigarettes, or pipes is prohibited.

Have Exact Fare Ready

- Local bus $1.15
- Express bus $4.00

To Exit Bus Via Rear Passenger Door:

- Passenger signal ◖≣
- Wait for light.
- Push door handle to open.
- Hold on to door handle until clear of step.

Passenger Operated Safety Exit.

Danger:

Do not stand in step well while bus is in motion.
To open door, push handle on door.
Stand clear.

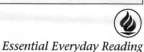

METRO BUS SERVICE

1. What fare would each of the following people pay to ride a local Metro bus?

   (a) A 15-year-old high school student: _____

   (b) A 65-year-old woman: _____

   (c) A downtown office worker: _____

   (d) A 50-year-old grandfather: _____

   (e) A 25-year-old college student: _____

   (f) A young man in a wheelchair: _____

   (g) A mother with a baby and a six-year-old: _____

   (h) A father with three children under the age of five: _____

2. What fare would you pay to ride an express bus? _____

3. Put an X next to each of the following actions that breaks one of Metro Bus's rules.

   _____ (a) Akeem chatters to the bus driver, insisting that she talk with him.

   _____ (b) Samantha waits for the rear passenger door to open for her.

   _____ (c) Art brings an unlit cigar onto the bus.

   _____ (d) Max drops a $1 bill, a dime, and a nickel into the fare box.

   _____ (e) Nicole pushes the rear passenger door open and gets off.

   _____ (f) Justin stands down on the step next to the rear passenger door when the bus gets close to his stop.

What Do You Think?

4. Would you rather take a bus to get around a city, or drive your own car? Why?

   _____

   _____

   _____

   _____

47 *Essential Everyday Reading*

[You can win a big prize if you can get through to an out-of-town radio station within the next 93 seconds. You've got to figure out in a hurry how to dial!]

Pay Phone

5¢–10¢–25¢
U.S. Coins only.

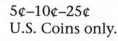 Coin Release

NORTHEAST TELEPHONE

Calls within this area code:

Local Cash Calls	Deposit 20¢ before dialing.
Other Calls	See specific dialing instructions.
Emergencies	Dial 0. No coin needed.
Long Distance Calls Outside This Area	See long-distance dialing instructions.

Northeast Telephone calls within this area code:

- **Calling Card Calls**   0 + Number
  From Touch-Tone Phones:
      Wait for tone, then dial calling card number.
      To make additional calls within the area code,
          do not hang up, push # button and dial next call.
- **From Rotary Phone:**   0 + Number
      After tone, wait for Operator.
  If you would like to order a Northeast
      Telephone Co. Calling Card, call toll free   1-800-555-5000

- **Cash Calls**   1 + Number
- **Collect & Person-to-Person Calls**   0 + Number
- **Repair** (Dial Free)   1-555-1611
- **Directory Assistance Calls**   1-555-1212

Long Distance Calls Outside This Area Code

- **Coin Calls**   1 + Area Code + Number
      handled by AT&T Long Distance Service
- **Other Calls**   0 +Area Code + Number
      handled by PhoneCharge Inc.
  If you wish to use a different long-distance company, dial their access code and
  proceed as directed by them.

  Rate information available on request.

PAY PHONE DIRECTIONS

■ For each of the following, tell what you must dial.

1. You are calling home from your school, a local call.

   _____

2. The phone isn't working right.

   _____

3. You are making a toll call in this area code and are paying cash for it.

   _____

4. You only want to speak to one particular person.

   _____

5. You are making a long-distance call on a touch-tone phone in this area code, and you're paying for it with your calling card.

   _____

6. After you finish call 5 above, you want to make another long-distance call in this area code.

   _____

7. There's been a traffic accident, and you need to call for an ambulance.

   _____

8. You need to call home, but it's a toll call and you don't have any cash to pay for the call. You don't have a calling card, either.

   _____

9. You are making a long-distance call out of this area code and are paying cash for it.

   _____

(continued)

PAY PHONE DIRECTIONS *(CONTINUED)*

10. You are making a long-distance call on a rotary phone, using your calling card.

   _____

11. You don't know the phone number of the person you want to call.

   _____

What Do You Think?

12. What is the difference between a touch-tone phone and a rotary phone?

   _____

   _____

   _____

   _____

   _____

13. Do you have a phone company calling card? Why or why not?

   _____

   _____

   _____

   _____

   _____

   _____

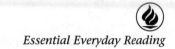

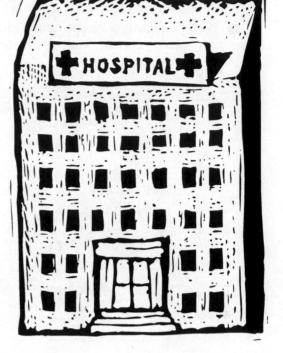

Adult Medical and Surgical Units

Weekdays: noon to 2:00 P.M. and 6:00 to 8:00 P.M.
Weekends and holidays: noon to 8:00 P.M.

Pediatric Unit

Parents and grandparents: anytime.
Others: 8:00 A.M. to 8:00 P.M. every day.

Special Care Unit

Immediate family only: five minutes once in each hour from 10:00 A.M. to 10:00 P.M. every day.

Cardiac Intensive Care Unit

Immediate family only: five minutes once in each hour, 24 hours a day every day.

Labor/Delivery

Fathers or support persons for the delivery are welcome at any time.
Family members or close friends may attend after delivery as the parents wish.
Siblings who attend during delivery are are required to have a preparatory session first.

Psychiatric Unit

Weekdays: 6:00 to 8:00 P.M.
Weekends and holidays: 10:00 A.M. to 8:00 P.M.

Maternity Unit and Newborn Nursery

Fathers/support persons: anytime until 10:00 P.M.
Immediate family: noon to 6:00 P.M.
Others: 7:00 to 8:00 P.M.
Children under 12 may visit only if siblings to the new baby.

HOSPITAL VISITING HOURS

■ Write **Yes** or **No** next to each situation below, depending on whether the person can or cannot visit the patient, according to the hospital's visiting rules. If the answer is **No**, tell why.

_____ 1. Letitia wants to visit her brother, who is being treated for mental problems. It is Monday at 4 P.M.

_____

_____

_____ 2. Rosa wants to visit her 6-year-old granddaughter even though it's 11 P.M.

_____

_____

_____ 3. Karen wants to visit her husband, who has just had a heart attack and is in intensive care, before she goes to work, at 7 A.M. Tuesday.

_____

_____

_____ 4. Now Karen's mother wants to visit Karen's husband at 7:30 A.M. Tuesday.

_____

_____

_____ 5. Tom wants to visit his best friend, who is 13 years old, at 2 P.M. Saturday.

_____

_____

_____ 6. Bart's aunt wants to visit Bart in the special care unit at 10 A.M. Sunday.

_____

_____

(continued)

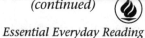

HOSPITAL VISITING HOURS *(CONTINUED)*

_____ 7. Frank wants to see his newborn twins at 9 P.M.

      _____

      _____

_____ 8. Lonnie, age 10, wants to see his new baby brothers, too, at 5 P.M.

      _____

      _____

_____ 9. Lonnie's 8-year-old cousin wants to come along to see the twins.

      _____

      _____

_____ 10. Jenna wants to see her mother, who is being treated for a broken leg. It is Thursday at 4 P.M.

      _____

      _____

_____ 11. By the time Julio arrives at the hospital, his wife is almost ready to deliver their baby.

      _____

      _____

What Do You Think?

12. Why do hospitals limit visiting hours?

      _____

      _____

13. Do you think the listed visiting hours are reasonable? What changes would you make in them, if any?

      _____

      _____

      _____

      _____

Note: These are self-service machines. Please check before using. We are not responsible for articles left in them. No dyeing of clothes allowed in machines. Thank you.

Washing Machine

A warning for your safety:

- Do not reach into the washtub until all moving parts have stopped.
- Disconnect electric power before servicing, to reduce the risk of shock.
- Do not let children play on or around the washer.
- Do not put flammable cleaning solvents or items that are damp with these solvents in the washer.

To operate washer, lid must be closed

1. Measure detergent into washtub.
2. Load dry clothes loosely into washtub.
3. Close lid.
4. Set wash temperature and/or fabric selector switches.
5. Place coins in coin slot. If slide, push in, then pull out.
6. Add fabric softener when Rinse light comes on.

If Unbalanced Load light comes on, open lid, make sure washer has stopped spinning, and then rearrange clothes. Close lid to start spin cycle again.

Washer—Up to 50 Pounds

$3
Insert 12 quarters.

For towels, sheets, blankets, bedspreads, shag rugs.
No pillows of any kind.

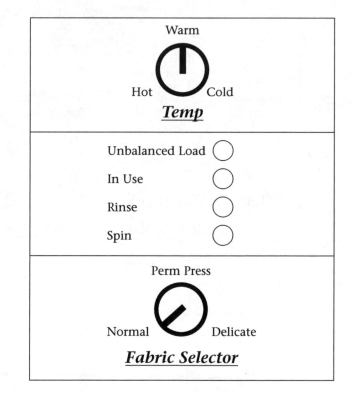

Warm

Hot — Cold
Temp

Unbalanced Load ◯

In Use ◯

Rinse ◯

Spin ◯

Perm Press

Normal — Delicate
Fabric Selector

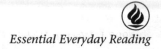

SELF-SERVICE LAUNDRY

1. Put a check (✓) next to each thing you should/may do when using the washing machine. Cross out the things you should/may **not** do.

   _____ (a) Rearrange clothes while the machine is running.

   _____ (b) Measure detergent and put it in the washtub.

   _____ (c) Choose the type of fabric.

   _____ (d) Put in clothes that you have pretreated with a flammable cleaning solvent.

   _____ (e) Add dye to the washtub.

   _____ (f) Rearrange clothes if the Unbalanced Load light comes on.

   _____ (g) Demand that the management pay you for a sweater you left in the washer.

   _____ (h) When the Rinse light comes on, add fabric softener.

   _____ (i) Wash your bedspread and blanket in the 50-pound washer.

   _____ (j) Wash your pillows in the 50-pound washer.

2. Number these steps in the correct order for operating the washing machine.

   ____ Insert coins in slot.   ____ Set wash temperature.

   ____ Close lid.   ____ Load clothes into washtub.

   ____ Add detergent to washtub.   ____ Add fabric softener.

What Do You Think?

3. Why shouldn't children play on or around washer? _____

   _____

4. Give a few examples of clothes for which you would choose the following cycles:

   Normal: _____

   Permanent Press: _____

   Delicate: _____

[You have arrived at the campground just 15 minutes before it will be too late to register for the night and set up camp. You have to read these rules quickly.]

Regulations for Use of Campground

- All campers must stop and register upon arrival. Campers may check in after 1:00 P.M. and must check out before 11:00 A.M.

- If you have reserved your campsite in advance, you must bring your reservation confirmation slip to the camper registration booth to complete your registration.

- Campers are not allowed to set up camp after 10:00 P.M.

- Check the site map and select the campsite you prefer. Be sure the site is large enough to accommodate your party and all your equipment.

- Minimum length of stay is two (2) nights. Maximum length of stay is fourteen (14) nights. The campground is open from May 15 through September 15.

- No water or electrical hookups are available. Running water is available from spigots at the locations marked *W* on your site map.

- Each campsite is limited to one camping party, which means:

(a) A family consisting of father, mother, and any number of their unmarried children.

(b) Up to six (6) individuals, including children, using one camping setup.

(c) Not more than two (2) vehicles per campsite, including visitors.

- Campsite visitors are allowed only from 9:00 A.M. until 8:00 P.M. Visitors must pay

the campground visitor fee. Limit one (1) visiting party to a campsite, with the total number of visiting people not to exceed ten (10).

- Pets are allowed only if kept leashed or otherwise restrained. They must not be left unattended. Pet owners must immediately clean up any fecal deposits left by their pets.

- Quiet is required between the hours of 10:00 P.M. and 7:00 A.M.

- Open fires are allowed only in grills or fireplaces provided at each campsite. Do not leave any fires unattended. Use only already fallen and dead branches; do not cut trees or branches from trees for burning.

- We provide no trash bins. We have a carry-in-carry-out waste policy: **Everything** you carry in you also carry out. You must dispose of your waste matter yourself. Burn paper or wood products (paper plates, cups, egg cartons, napkins, cereal boxes) and carry out all other waste matter (plastics, polystyrene, glass, aluminum, tin, batteries, and disposable razors and lighters).

- Hunting is not allowed. The use of chain saws and power equipment is also prohibited.

CAMPGROUND RULES

■ Each of these campers is breaking one of the campground rules. Tell what each camper is doing wrong.

1. Six high school seniors are sharing one campsite with three tents.

   _____

   _____

2. Two cars of visitors have joined the campers at Site 10.

   _____

   _____

3. Tom and Jerry play their portable stereo until midnight.

   _____

   _____

4. The campers at Site 3 put all their garbage in a plastic bag and leave it at the camper registration booth when they leave.

   _____

   _____

   _____

5. Yvette and Shanna start packing up to leave their campsite at noon.

   _____

   _____

6. Matt and Nate plan to arrive at 11 P.M. and set up camp quickly.

   _____

   _____

(continued)

CAMPGROUND RULES *(CONTINUED)*

7. Elizabeth uses her chain saw to cut trees for firewood.

   _____

   _____

8. The campers at Site 7 arrived on July 5. It is now July 21.

   _____

   _____

9. Omar, Jim, and Chris are sharing a campsite. Each drove his own car to the campground.

   _____

   _____

10. Toni and Bill's friends from the nearby town are visiting their campsite at 10 P.M.

    _____

    _____

What Do You Think?

11. Do you think a carry-in/carry-out waste policy makes sense? Why or why not?

    _____

    _____

    _____

    _____

    _____

How to Conduct a Search
Using This Terminal

To Find a Title:

1. At the Title? prompt, press the **F1** key.

2. Type in the title.

3. Press the **F3** key.

To halt the scroll, press the **F4** key. The Call Number is on the second line of the record.

(Call numbers only appear for nonfiction.)

To resume scrolling, press any key.

To begin another search, press any key. Then press **F5**. After message appears on screen, press **F6**.

To Find a Subject:

1. At the Title? prompt, press the **F2** key.

2. Type in the subject.

3. Press the **F3** key.

To halt the scroll, press the **F4** key. The Call Number is on the second line of the record.

(Call numbers only appear for nonfiction.)

To resume scrolling, press any key.

To begin another search, press any key. Then press **F5**. After message appears on screen, press **F6**.

Use This Terminal To:

1. Find the call number of a nonfiction title.

2. Find the general call number for a particular subject.

It is not possible to search by author.

General Instructions:

Title? must appear on the screen to begin a search. If necessary, press the **Esc** key until it appears.

If you make a mistake, pressing the **Enter** key will enable you to start over.

To halt scrolling, press **F4**. Press any key to continue scrolling.

If you cannot find the item you're looking for on the shelf, please inquire at the Information Desk on Level 2.

To Start a New Search:

1. Press the **Esc** key.

2. Press **F5**.

3. Wait for message on screen.

4. Press **F6**.

If the screen is blank, press the **Esc** key.

COMPUTER SEARCH DIRECTIONS

1. Tell why you press each of these keys.

   F1 _____

   F2 _____

   F3 _____

   F4 _____

   F5 _____

   F6 _____

   Enter _____

   Esc _____

2. When can you start a new search? _____

3. What should you do if you can't find the book you want on the shelf?

   _____

4. What is a book's call number? How does this help you find the book?

   _____

5. What kind of book doesn't have a call number? _____

   How can you find this book? _____

   _____

6. What should you do if the screen is blank? _____

   _____

What Do You Think?

7. What should you do if you want to look up an author's name?

   _____

8. What does **Esc** stand for? _____ Why is that word used for this key?

   _____

9. What do you think appears on the screen after you type in a subject and press **F3**?

   _____

Name _____

Date _____

Unit 5. Consumerism

Being a skillful consumer means reading information carefully: What does that sweepstakes offer really say? How do you return your bottles? What services does this store offer? If you need help or want to buy something, look up the information in the phone book or classified ads. Practice this kind of reading here. First, get to know some of the vocabulary words in this section. Write the correct word from the following list on the blank next to its definition below.

abuse	certificate	guarantee	redeem
anonymous	crisis	nominal	reject
automatic	eligible	partial	unusual
beverage	fraud	radius	welfare

_____ 1. Line from the center to the outside curve of a circle

_____ 2. Existing in name or form only

_____ 3. To return something for money

_____ 4. A liquid for drinking

_____ 5. To refuse to accept

_____ 6. Self-moving or self-acting

_____ 7. Document that says something is true

_____ 8. Qualified to be chosen; entitled

_____ 9. Assurance that something exists or will be done

_____ 10. Relating to a part rather than the whole thing

_____ 11. An unstable, very important time

_____ 12. Help, assistance

_____ 13. Trickery, cheating

_____ 14. Having or giving no name

_____ 15. Bad treatment

_____ 16. Uncommon, very different

Homeowner's Headquarters

We Are Here to Help You

Free Services

- Cut electrical wire, window shades, glass, and two cuts of lumber and plywood

- Custom color paint tinting

- Professional advice and do-it-yourself booklets

- Tie-down twine and clearance flags for long loads

Free Home Delivery

- Purchases over $400

- Bath/kitchen projects

- Building packages

Delivery Schedule:

Zone A   Monday and Thursday

Zone B   Tuesday and Friday

Zone C   Wednesday and Saturday

Next Day Delivery Available

- Purchases of $400 or more, within a 30-mile radius

- Purchases under $400, at a nominal charge

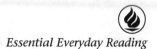

SERVICE DESK INFORMATION

1. Will Homeowner's Headquarters do these things for you? Check the correct column, **Yes** or **No**.

	Yes	No
(a) Deliver $300 of bath project materials, free		
(b) Give you twine to tie down your materials in your car		
(c) Deliver $300 of yard equipment, free		
(d) Custom tint your paint		
(e) Cut window glass		
(f) Cut a sheet of plywood into eight pieces, free		
(g) Deliver the next day to your home, which is 40 miles away		
(h) Give you red flags for a long load		
(i) Deliver $200 of roof shingles for a small charge		
(j) Give you unlimited free advice		

2. You live in Zone B. You buy materials on Saturday. What day will your materials be delivered? _____

3. You live in Zone A. You buy materials late Monday afternoon. What day will your materials be delivered? _____

4. You live in Zone C. You buy materials on Thursday. What day will your materials be delivered? _____

What Do You Think?

5. Why do you think Homewoner's Headquarters offers free delivery?

_____

6. What do you consider to be a "nominal" charge for delivery?

_____

How much would you be willing to pay for delivery of something?

_____

[You've got two bags of bottles and cans to return. Your very impatient brother is waiting in his car outside. If you don't get these bottles processed fast, you're going to lose your ride home.]

- Please redeem your returnable **beverage cans** and **plastic bottles** at the redemption machines.

- Our service clerks will redeem your returnable **glass bottles** at the bottle return area.

- We will gladly accept any rejected beverage cans, plastic bottles, gallon plastic beverage containers, or glass bottles at the bottle return window.

Thank you.

Aluminum Cans Only

Our self-service can redemption unit will accept soda and beer cans, and most small juice cans.

- Put all cans into round hole.
- Try rejected cans again.
- Press rounded green square.
- Pull receipt straight toward you. Receipt will tear automatically.

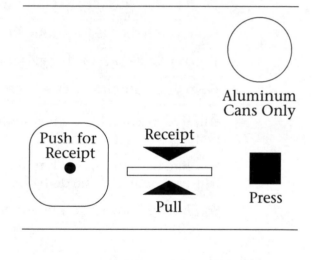

Plastic Bottles Only

Our self-service bottle redemption unit will accept plastic bottles and plastic beverage containers.

- Put all plastics into round hole, bottom end first.
- Try rejected plastic containers again.
- Press red square.
- Pull receipt straight toward you. Receipt will tear automatically.

Pre GED

lesson today
1/26/2016

ᴛᴛʟᴇ ᴀɴᴅ ᴄᴀɴ ᴀᴇᴄʏᴄʟɪɴɢ

1. _____ steps in the correct order for using the redemption machines.

   _____ Try a rejected can again.

   _____ Pull out your receipt.

   _____ Press the colored square.

   _____ Put cans into the round hole.

2. What differences are there between the instructions for the aluminum can machine and the plastic bottle machine?

   _____

3. Where should you return the following items?

   (a) small juice cans _____

   (b) gallon plastic containers _____

   (c) glass bottles _____

   (d) beer cans _____

   (e) soda cans _____

What Do You Think?

4. What should you do with your receipt once you have taken it from the machine?

   _____

5. Why would a store install bottle/can redemption machines?

   _____

6. What are the benefits of recycling? _____

   _____

7. What other materials can be recycled? _____

   _____

8. What materials do you recycle? _____

   _____

Dear Friend,

Congratulations! If your Personal Prize Number on the enclosed Sweepstakes Certificate is the winning number—

you have won **five million dollars!**

But there's a catch: You have to return your winning certificate to be eligible to win the five million dollar prize. Don't delay! Send your entry today.

Sad to say, some winners don't return their Sweepstakes Certificates—and they lose their prize! Think how badly you'd feel if your Five Million Dollars were awarded to someone else—just because you didn't return your winning Personal Prize Number Sweepstakes Certificate.

So don't delay. Tear out your preaddressed Personal Prize Number Certificate now. Put it in the mail today. Then get ready to spend your millions!

We have another treat for you. Why not order some of our guaranteed, high-quality merchandise while you're returning your Sweepstakes Certificate? Just put your Certificate in the YES envelope along with your merchandise order form. We'll give your order and your Sweepstakes entry top priority.

A word of caution. As you know, postal rates are skyrocketing. We may be forced to cut back on our mailing list, and the first names we'll drop will be people who never order from our exciting gift catalog. So order now to be sure you remain on our Sweepstakes mailing list! You'll be delighted with every item you order—we guarantee it!

Sincerely,

All-American Sweepstakes and Gift Company

P.S. Remember: Every day counts! Don't put your entry aside. Mail it today so you don't forget. <u>Five million dollars</u> is at stake!

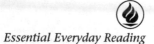

SWEEPSTAKES NOTICE

1. Write **True** or **False** next to each statement about the sweepstakes offer.

_____ (a) This letter tells you that you have already won five million dollars.

_____ (b) You must return your winning certificate right away in order to win a prize.

_____ (c) The company guarantees you will be satisfied with any items you order from it.

_____ (d) You will be dropped from the sweepstakes mailing list if you do not order some gifts from the company's catalog.

_____ (e) You cannot win a prize if you don't return your prize certificate.

_____ (f) Use the YES envelope if you are ordering something from the catalog.

_____ (g) You are the only person who has your Personal Prize Number.

_____ (h) Your chances of winning are better if you order some items from the gift catalog.

2. How does the sweepstakes company make this letter look interesting and catch your attention?

_____

What Do You Think?

3. Is it worthwhile to spend the time and the postage money to return your Prize Certificate to the sweepstakes company? Why or why not?

_____

4. Why do companies run sweepstakes like this one?

_____

5. Do you think anything about this letter is misleading? Explain.

_____

ARTICLES FOR SALE—MISC.	GARAGE SALES
19" COLOR TV w/ remote, $110. 999-8484	**DAY STREET #203.** Baby clothing & furniture, toys, kitchen equip. Sat. 9-5.
BOOKCASE - 5' X 6' X 13'. $75. 989-2233	**GRANT ROAD #14.** 2 family, furniture, records, sports equip, tools, dishes, books, clothing. Sat-Sun 10-4.
CEMETERY PLOTS - Spring Grove, 2 side-by-side plots, 10% discount. 727-3311	
CUSTOM-MADE king-size headboard, carved maple. $500 or best offer. 876-9500	**HIGH STREET #32.** Something for everyone. Collectibles, books, old coins, small appliances. Fri., Sat. 9-5.
G.E. WASHER & DRYER. Used one year only. $300 each, or $500 for both. 977-4675	**HIGH STREET #233.** Go-cart, vanity, refrig/freezer, yard tools, much more. Sat. 9-3.
INVISIBLE FENCE SYSTEM w/ 2 collars. Great deal! $500. Call 838-3211 soon.	**KENILWORTH CIRCLE #5.** Antiques, paintings, Oriental rugs, craft & canning supplies, good furniture, more. Fri-Sat-Sun 10-4.
RIDING LAWN MOWER, 10 hp, self-bagger, 32 in. cut, exc. condition. Best offer over $350. 929-3030	
WHEELCHAIR RAMP - with railing, 20 ft. long, $95. Also 20 wooden fence posts, $35. 337-5679	**LINCOLN ST. #45.** Air conditioner, gas dryer, kitchen items, tools, bikes, etc. Sat. 10-4, Sun. 10-3.
	ROUTE ONE SO. #244. Little bit of everything for everyone. Sat. 8-4.
	SAWYER ST. #97. Lots of unusual items— don't miss this one! Sat.-Sun. 9-4.
	Advertise in the Classifieds

CLASSIFIED ADS

1. Which yard sale(s) would you go to, or what number(s) would you call, if you wanted to buy the following items?

   (a) bedroom furniture _____

   (b) fencing material _____

   (c) kids' stuff _____

   (d) clothes dryer _____

   (e) small appliances _____

   (f) lawn mower _____

   (g) bookcase _____

   (h) coins _____

   (i) kitchen equipment _____

   (j) TV set _____

   (k) books _____

   (l) tools _____

2. What do these abbreviations stand for?

   (a) MISC. _____

   (b) w/ _____

   (c) in. _____

   (d) exc. _____

   (e) ft. _____

   (f) equip. _____

   (g) refrig. _____

(continued)

CLASSIFIED ADS (CONTINUED)

What Do You Think?

3. What are the advantages of buying things at a yard sale or from a private individual instead of at a store?

    _____

    _____

    _____

    What are the disadvantages? _____

    _____

    _____

4. Where in your community would you find notices of yard sales and items for sale by individuals?

    _____

    _____

    _____

    _____

5. Check out any items you and members of your family have that you no longer need or use. Could you have a yard sale to dispose of these items and earn some money?

    _____

    _____

    _____

    _____

    _____

Use this guide to help you find services and information you need from community service organizations—both government and nonprofit agencies. This is only a partial listing. Call the State Citizens' Information Line for more information: 1-800-222-2222.

Crisis

(Lines answered 24 hours a day.)
Adult & Child Abuse
. . . . toll-free 1-800-334-8888
Alcoholics Anonymous 929-9999
Family Crisis Shelter. 929-0033
Rape Crisis 927-0000
Suicide Prevention 927-1345

Alcohol/Drug Abuse

Alanon 927-3311
Alcoholics Anonymous 929-9999
Day One 883-0122

Animal Welfare

Animal Refuge League 883-6754
ASPCA 927-0976

Consumer Protection

Better Business Bureau 767-9343
Bureau of Banking 655-8766
Consumer Fraud Bureau 655-0171
Insurance Board 655-4211
Real Estate Board 656-0987

Environmental Protection

Department of Environmental Protection
. . . . 688-7644
Hazardous Substances Spills 688-5544
Water Testing Office 655-4387

Family Services and Counseling

Abuse/Neglect Hot Line
. . . . toll free 1-800-334-8888
Community Counseling Center . 929-2211
Divorce Perspectives 927-3458
Kids to Kids 925-8998
Parents & Kids Center 925-6653
Overeaters Anonymous 929-7633
Planned Parenthood 927-0154

Food

Food Stamps 927-0058
Meals on Wheels 767-5959
Salvation Army 766-0948

Health

AIDS Line 929-4657
. . . . toll free 1-899-853-0099
Community Health Center 927-8315
Medicaid Information 688-0978
Public Health Nursing 929-3030

Housing

Housing Authority 929-7766

TELEPHONE HELP LINES

■ For each situation, tell which organization(s) you would call for help.

1. A stray dog needs a home.

   _____

2. Your elderly neighbor can't prepare her own meals.

   _____

3. You can't seem to control your urge to eat all the time.

   _____

4. You're worried about being exposed to AIDS.

   _____

5. You're having trouble finding an apartment you can afford.

   _____

6. A con artist has tricked you into buying driveway sealer that washes right off.

   _____

7. Your older sister has a drinking problem.

   _____

8. Your roommate has been raped.

   _____

9. You find out that your best friend is being abused at home.

   _____

10. An oil delivery truck overturns, spilling fuel into a stream.

    _____

(continued)

TELEPHONE HELP LINES (CONTINUED)

11. You have a problem that you need to talk to another kid about.

   _____

12. Your neighbor keeps a dog chained up outside with no shelter in all kinds of weather.

   _____

13. You want some information about birth control.

   _____

14. Even though you have a job, you don't have enough money to buy the food you need.

   _____

15. The water in your home smells and tastes strange.

   _____

16. You think about suicide.

   _____

What Do You Think?

17. What kinds of services does a family crisis center offer?

   _____

   _____

   _____

18. Where would you find a listing of telephone help lines for your area?

   _____

UNIT 6. FOOD

Do you need to read to eat? Yes! Read package directions and microwave instructions to cook. Read labels and menus to know what you're buying and eating. Practice this kind of reading here. First, get to know some of the vocabulary words in this section. Write the correct word from the following list on the blank next to the word's definition below.

automatic	entree	nutrition	sautéed
casserole	gelatin	operation	set
defrost	ingredient	requirement	simmer
dissolve	invert	restaurant	utensil

_____ 1. Substance used as the basis of jelly and glues; also, an edible jelly made of this substance

_____ 2. To melt, or to turn into a liquid

_____ 3. To become firm or solid

_____ 4. Something that is part of a combination or mixture

_____ 5. To turn inside or upside down

_____ 6. Dish in which food is cooked and served

_____ 7. To cook slowly just below the boiling point

_____ 8. Process of taking in and using food in the body

_____ 9. To thaw out from a frozen state

_____ 10. A kitchen tool

_____ 11. Done in a self-moving or self-acting way

_____ 12. Something needed or essential

_____ 13. A public eating place

_____ 14. Cooked by frying in a small amount of fat

_____ 15. Main dish of the meal

_____ 16. Method of using a machine

The Corsican Welcomes You

Salads

Small $1.95   Large $3.95

Tossed   Lettuce, tomato, green peppers, onions, black olives, creamy Italian dressing

Greek   Spinach, tomato, onions, mushrooms, cauliflower, feta cheese, with lemon anchovy dressing

Chef's   Garden salad with roasted turkey, ham, cheeses, and choice of dressings $5.50

Dressings

Creamy italian, lemon anchovy, curry mustard, creamy dill, spicy red vinaigrette, buttermilk/basil/garlic

Calzones

Pizza crust folded over tasty stuffing

Italian   Spinach, onions, and parmesan, mozzarella, ricotta, and provolone cheeses, with pizza sauce on the side $4.75

Greek   Broccoli, onions, mushrooms, feta cheese, and grated provolone and mozzarella, with pizza sauce on the side $4.75

French   Turkey, broccoli, onion, and boursin cheese (a cream cheese and garlic spread) .. $5.50

Corsican   Tender roast beef, sautéed onions, mushrooms, and grated provolone and mozzarella, served with a sour cream and horseradish sauce $5.50

Sandwiches

Made on our own fresh home-baked dill bread and served with chips

Turkey Avocado Sandwich   Fresh roasted turkey meat, thick slices of ripe avocado, and sprouts, topped with our own creamy Italian dressing $4.95

Roast Beef Sub   Tender roast beef served with lettuce, tomatoes, with a garlic and cream cheese spread $4.95

Smoked Ham   and Swiss cheese sandwich accented with mustard $4.95

Veggie Sub   Fresh green leaf lettuce, tomatoes, onions, green peppers, dill pickles, black olives, and sprouts, topped with tangy, creamy Italian dressing and cheddar cheese $4.95

Meatball Sub   Real homemade meatballs made with hamburg, onions, green peppers, garlic, and Italian spices, covered with a rich tomato sauce and melted provolone cheese $4.95

Seafood

Seafood sandwiches served with a cup of homemade clam chowder or soup of the day

Lobster Sandwich   Tender lobster meat with mayonnaise and lettuce $9.95

Crab Sandwich   Fresh crabmeat with mayonnaise and lettuce $8.95

Vegetable Entrees

Burrito   Flour tortilla filled with vegetables, Spanish brown rice, beans, and salsa, topped with lettuce, tomato, cheese, and sour cream .. $5.95

Eggplant Lasagna   A four-cheese lasagna with eggplant, spinach, mushrooms, green peppers, and onions with our own delicious tomato sauce, served with tossed green salad and home-baked garlic bread $6.95

Essential Everyday Reading

RESTAURANT MENU

1. According to the menu, what is a calzone? _____

   _____

2. What would you order if you wanted to eat seafood? _____

   _____

3. Which salad would you order if you wanted one with meat? _____

   _____

4. If you were a person who ate no meat, what items could you order from this menu?

   _____

   _____

5. If you order a non-seafood sandwich, what do you get with it?

   _____

6. If you order a seafood sandwich, what do you get with it?

   _____

7. Which items on this menu do **not** contain cheese?

   _____

8. What ingredients do the Greek items on this menu have in common?

   _____

9. What is the cheapest item on this menu? _____

   What is the most expensive item? _____

What Do You Think?

10. Which of the sandwiches would you order? _____

    Which calzone would you order? _____

11. Do you think this is a fairly healthy selection of things to eat? Why or why not?

    _____

[You've got to order quickly. The movie you're going to see starts in just 20 minutes.]

Potato Skins $2.79

Pizza Style $3.49
Veggie Style $3.49
Mexi Style $3.49
Burger Style $3.69
Extra Topping . . . . $ .89

Spinach-Cheese Souffle $3.29
Mushroom-Cheese Souffle $3.29
Tex-Mex Chili $3.59
Hot Dog $2.99
Chili Dog $3.49

Sandwiches

Meatball $3.49
Saucy Chicken $3.49
Pepper Steak $3.89

Croissants

Ham 'n' Cheese $3.29
Spinach 'n' Cheese $3.29
Chicken 'n' Broccoli $3.49

Burgers

Regular. $3.29
Cheese $3.49
Double $3.99
Double w/Cheese $4.29
Chili. $4.29

Beverages

Coke.	$.79	$.99
Diet Coke	$.79	$.99
Sprite	$.79	$.99
Diet Sprite	$.79	$.99
Orange	$.79	$.99
Lemonade	$.79	$.99
Ice Tea	$.79	$.99
Coffee	$.79	$.99
Tea	$.79	$.99
Milk	$.79	$.99
French Fries	$.89	$1.29

FAST-FOOD MENU

1. What is the most expensive burger on the menu?

   _____

   What is the cheapest burger?

   _____

2. What would regular potato skins with extra topping cost?

   _____

3. What is the most expensive sandwich on the menu?

   _____

4. What is the cheapest food (not drink) on the menu?

   _____

5. If you have only $5 to spend (before tax), can you afford:

   (a) a chili dog, fries, and a drink? _____

   (b) a hot dog, fries, and a drink? _____

   (c) Mexi style potato skins and a large drink? _____

   (d) Mexi style potato skins with extra topping and a small drink? _____

What Do You Think?

6. What's the difference between a spinach and cheese soufflé and a spinach
   and cheese croissant?

   _____

   _____

   _____

   _____

Directions: Add 1 cup (8 oz) boiling water to contents of this package. Stir until completely dissolved, about 2 minutes. Add 1 cup cold water. Chill until set. Makes 4 servings, $\frac{1}{2}$ cup each.

Speed Set: Add $\frac{3}{4}$ cup boiling water to contents of this package. Stir until completely dissolved. Combine $\frac{1}{2}$ cup cold water and ice cubes to make $1\frac{1}{4}$ cups ice and water. Add to dissolved gelatin. Stir until slightly thickened, then remove any unmelted ice. Chill. Soft-set and ready to eat in 30 minutes.

To Add Fruits and Vegetables: Chill gelatin until slightly thickened, then gently mix in 1 to $1\frac{1}{2}$ cups. (Do not add fresh or frozen pineapple/kiwi fruit. Canned or cooked pineapple can be used.) Chill until set.

To Mold Gelatin: Add only $\frac{3}{4}$ cup cold water to dissolved gelatin. Chill in mold until firm (3 hours). To remove from mold, dip briefly (10 seconds) to rim in warm water. Shake to loosen. Put wet plate on top of mold. Invert plate and mold together. Remove mold.

GELATIN DESSERT DIRECTIONS

1. Write the amount of water you add to the gelatin:

    (a) using the regular directions _____

    (b) using a mold _____

    (c) using the speed set method _____

2. Write the amount of time it takes for the gelatin to set:

    (a) if you use a mold _____

    (b) if you use the regular way to make it _____

3. Why would you use the speed-set method of making this dessert?

    _____

    _____

    _____

4. What two ingredients should you **not** add to this gelatin?

    _____

    _____

What Do You Think?

5. List some ingredients you like to add to gelatin dessert, or would like to try adding.

    _____

    _____

    _____

    _____

SCALLOPED POTATO DIRECTIONS

Makes 6 servings, 1/2 cup each

Oven Method

Heat: Oven to 400°.

Pour: Potato slices and sauce mix into ungreased 2½-quart casserole.

Stir In: 2 tablespoons margarine or butter and 3 cups **boiling** water, stirring until butter is melted.

Add: 1 cup milk; stir until well mixed.

Bake: Uncovered until potatoes are tender and lightly browned, 30 to 35 minutes. Let stand several minutes before serving, while sauce thickens.

Stove-Top Method

Combine and Heat: 2 tablespoons margarine or butter and 3 cups water in 2- or 3-quart saucepan. Bring to a boil.

Stir In: Potato slices.

Heat: To boiling, stirring frequently. Reduce heat to simmer; cook covered, stirring occasionally, until potatoes are tender, about 30 minutes.

Stir In: 1 cup milk and sauce mix.

Heat: 4 to 5 more minutes, stirring constantly, until sauce is thickened.

Microwave Method

Pour: Potato slices into ungreased 2-quart round microwave-safe casserole.

Stir In: 3 cups hot water and 2 tablespoons margarine or butter.

Microwave: Covered with waxed paper, on high (100%) 5 minutes.

Stir In: Sauce mix and 1 cup milk, mixing well.

Microwave: Covered, on high, 4 to 5 minutes longer until potatoes are tender.

Let Stand: 5 minutes while sauce thickens.

SCALLOPED POTATO DIRECTIONS

1. Check off the cooking method or methods that each of the following steps is part of.

	Oven	Stove Top	Microwave
(a) Use a 2-quart round casserole.			
(b) First, mix together the potato slices and sauce.			
(c) Let stand while sauce thickens.			
(d) Use a 2- or 3-quart saucepan.			
(e) Cover with wax paper.			
(f) Cook uncovered.			
(g) Stir occasionally.			
(h) Add the sauce mix and milk after 5 minutes of cooking.			
(i) Cook at a low temperature.			
(j) Cook at high energy or temperature.			
(k) Use a 2½-quart casserole.			

2. Write how long you should cook the potatoes:

    (a) using the oven method _____

    (b) using the stove top method _____

    (c) using the microwave method _____

3. How do you know when the potatoes are done? _____

What Do You Think?

4. Which method would you choose to cook these potatoes? _____

    Why? _____

    _____

    _____

Chunky Peanut Butter

Nutrition Facts

Serving Size: 2 tbsp (32 grams)
Servings per 12 oz Container: 10
Servings per 18 oz Container: 16

Ingredients

Selected U.S. Peanuts
Dextrose
Partially Hydrogenated Vegetable Oil
　(to prevent separation)
Salt
Sugar

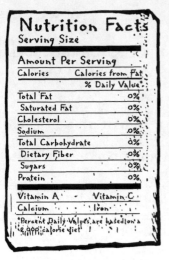

Amount per Serving Value*		% Daily
Calories	200	
Fat Calories	140	
Total Fat	17 grams	25%
Saturated Fat	3 grams	15%
Cholesterol	0 mg	0%
Sodium	120 mg	5%
Total Carbohydrate	5 grams	2%
Dietary Fiber	2 grams	7%
Sugars	3 grams	
Protein	7 grams	
Vitamin A　0%	Calcium　0%	
Vitamin C　0%	Iron　0%	

Enriched Thin Spaghetti

Nutrition Facts

Serv. Size	2 oz (56 G) dry
Serv. Per Pkg. (16 oz)	8

Ingredients

Durum Wheat Semolina, Farina.

Amount per Serving		% Daily Value*
Calories	200	
Fat calories	140	
Total Fat	1 g	2%
Saturated Fat	0 g	15%
Polyunsaturated Fat	1 g	
Monosaturated Fat	0 g	
Cholesterol	0 mg	0%
Sodium	0 mg	0%
Total Carbohydrate	42 grams	14%
Dietary Fiber	2 grams	7%
Sugars	3 grams	
Protein	7 grams	
Vitamin A 0%	Thiamin 30%
Vitamin C 0%	Riboflavin 10%
Calcium 0%	Niacin 15%
Iron 10%	

*Percent Daily Values are based on a 2,000-calorie diet.

NUTRITIONAL INFORMATION AND INGREDIENTS

1. Complete this chart using information from the peanut butter and spaghetti labels.

	Peanut Butter	Spaghetti
(a) Serving size		
(b) Calories		
(c) Protein (grams)		
(d) Carbohydrate (grams)		
(e) Total Fat (% of DV)		
(f) Cholesterol (% of DV)		
(g) Sodium (mg)		

2. Which food is best for a person on a low-salt diet? _____

3. Which food is a good source of some B vitamins (niacin, thiamine, riboflavin)?

4. Which food has the most fat? _____

5. Which food contains a type of sugar? _____

6. What vitamins are listed on these labels? _____

7. What minerals are listed on these labels? _____

What Do You Think?

8. Why are the ingredients listed on cans, jars, and boxes of food?

   _____

9. What role do these things play in a person's nutrition?

   (a) calories _____

   (b) protein _____

   (c) carbohydrates _____

   (d) fat _____

   (e) cholesterol _____

   (f) vitamins _____

   (g) minerals _____

Essential Everyday Reading

Features

- Easy operation and fast cooking
- 30-minute timer with automatic shutoff
- Perfect for defrosting
- Turntable for complete, even cooking
- One-touch button for opening door
- Compact size with ample volume
- See-through window for viewing cooking
- Removable tempered glass turntable
- Easy-to-clean coated steel cavity and cabinet

Operation

1. Plug power supply cord into standard 3-prong 15 amp. power outlet.
2. Place food in suitable utensil.
3. Open oven door.
4. Put utensil on glass turntable.
5. Turntable must always be in place during cooking.
6. Shut door so it is firmly closed.
7. Set defrost knob to desired position— "High" or "Defrost."
8. Set timer to desired time.
9. Microwave starts cooking.
10. Microwave energy turns off automatically when timer points to "Off."
11. Take out food.

Safety Points

- To prevent oven from operating with door open, appliance is fitted with safety door interlock switches. To inspect food during cooking time, simply open door. Oven will automatically stop cooking. To continue cooking, simply close door.
- To stop cooking, simply turn timer knob to "Off." Reset at any time during cooking by turning timer knob.
- Do **not** let timer continue to operate after removing food.
- Do **not** operate oven when empty.
- Do **not** attempt to operate with door open.
- Keep oven level.
- Leave glass turntable in oven during cooking.
- Have oven checked by service technician if it is dropped or damaged.
- Do not try to override safety interlock switches.

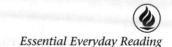

MICROWAVE OVEN

1. Check each thing you **should** do when using this microwave oven. Cross out each thing you should **not** do.

   _____ (a) Always operate with glass turntable in oven.

   _____ (b) Do not turn oven off in middle of cooking.

   _____ (c) Operate with door open.

   _____ (d) Open door by pressing button.

   _____ (e) Set timer for amount of cooking time you want.

   _____ (f) Run oven when it is empty to clean it.

   _____ (g) Reset cooking at any time with timer knob.

   _____ (h) Let timer run until it stops after you remove food from oven.

   _____ (i) Check on food during cooking by opening door.

2. Number these steps in the correct order for using this microwave.

   _____ Set timer for cooking time you want.

   _____ Shut door so it is firmly closed.

   _____ Take out food when timer points to "Off" and oven stops cooking.

   _____ Plug power cord in.

   _____ Set defrost knob to "High" or "Defrost."

   _____ Open oven door and put food container on turntable.

   _____ Place food in microwave-safe container.

What Do You Think?

3. How old should a child be before she or he is allowed to operate a micro-wave oven?

   _____

   Why? _____

4. What advantages are there to microwave cooking? _____

   _____

   What disadvantages? _____

UNIT 7. ENTERTAINMENT

Even if most of your entertainment is visual—things you see—you still need to read: to know how to play that video game, rent and take care of that video, choose that movie, load that film and get it developed.

Practice this kind of reading here. First, get to know some of the vocabulary words in this section. Write the correct word from the following list on the blank next to the word's definition below.

accompanied   deterioration   guardian   stationary
additional   ensure   permanent   subdued
appropriate   exposure   process   temporarily
compatible   format   repetitive   videocassette

_____ 1. Going along with

_____ 2. Correct, suitable

_____ 3. Happening over and over again

_____ 4. During a limited time

_____ 5. Going on without much change over time

_____ 6. Extra, increased

_____ 7. Develop film; produce slides or prints from exposed film

_____ 8. Not intense; tame

_____ 9. Amount of light that falls on film

_____ 10. Not moving

_____ 11. Shape, size, and general makeup

_____ 12. Make sure, certain, or safe

_____ 13. Act of growing worse

_____ 14. Able to work together

_____ 15. Plastic cartridge with a recording of a movie or television program

_____ 16. Person who is in charge of taking care of another person

Notice: Anyone under 16 years of age must be accompanied by parent or guardian.

Space Blasters

Object of Game

To capture enemy starfighters, saving universe and your own fleet.

To Start Game

1. See screen for scoring and bonus information.

2. Insert coin(s).

3. Select 1 or 2 players by pressing appropriate player button.

4. Use joystick to move starship. You have 10 starships.

5. Press "Blast" button to fire. Hold "Blast" button down for repetitive fire.

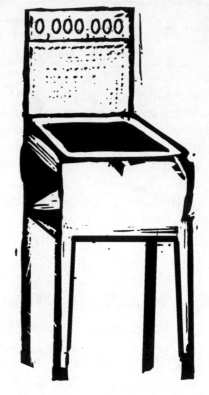

Action

- Hitting an enemy starfighter with laser beam disables and captures that starfighter.

- If no enemy starfighters are hit within a three-second period, captured starfighters are released.

- If your starship is hit by an enemy laser beam, that starship is captured and temporarily out of game.

- If your starship collides with an enemy, it is destroyed and permanently out of game.

- If you hit the enemy Mother Ship, your captured starships are released.

Scoring and Bonus Points

- Each enemy starfighter captured: 100 points.

- Each blue enemy starfighter captured: 500 points.

- Each red enemy starfighter captured: 750 points.

- If five enemy starfighters are captured within two seconds: 1,000 Bonus Points.

- Enemy Mother Ship hit: 10,000 Points.

- Each of your starships captured: –100 points.

- Each of your starships destroyed: –200 points.

VIDEO ARCADE

1. Number these steps in the correct order for starting the game:

   _____ Insert coins.

   _____ Press the "Blast" button to fire away.

   _____ Select the number of players.

   _____ Read the screen for scoring information.

   _____ Use the joystick to move your starship.

2. What causes your starship to be out of the game for a while?

   _____

3. What causes your starship to be destroyed and completely out of the game?

   _____

4. How can you get your captured starfighters released?

   _____

5. Figure out what your score will be based on the following:

   You capture two red starfighters.   _____

   You capture 10 regular starfighters.   _____

   Five of your starfighters are captured.   _____

   You hit the enemy Mother Ship.   _____

   Three of your starfighters are destroyed.   _____

   You capture one blue starfighter.   _____

   Twice, you capture five enemy starfighters
   within two seconds.   _____

   Total: _____

(continued)

VIDEO ARCADE (CONTINUED)

What Do You Think?

6. Why do you think kids under 16 aren't allowed in the arcade without an adult?

_____

_____

_____

_____

Do you think this is a reasonable rule? _____

_____

_____

Why or why not? _____

_____

_____

_____

_____

7. Why are most of the users of video arcades young males?

_____

_____

_____

_____

[You know a lot of movies are about to start. You've got to decide which one to see, fast, and get going to the right theater complex.]

Five-Star Theater	Route 7 Multiplex Cinema
Batman Returns (PG-13) M-F 1:00 7:10 9:50 S/S 1:00 4:20 7:10 9:50	*Nightmare on Elm Street XV* (R) Eves. 7:00 9:00 Mats. S/S 1:00 3:00
Barney! (G) M-F 12:20 7:15 S/S 12:10 2:15	*White Fang* (PG) Eves. 7:10 9:10 Mats. S/S 1:00 3:00
Kidnapped (R) M-F 7:00 9:45 S/S 7:00 9:45	*Wayne's World Goes Wild* (R) Eves. 7:15 9:15 Mats. S/S 1:15 3:15
From the Heart (PG) M-F 1:00 7:25 9:50 S/S 1:00 3:45 7:25 9:50	*Home Alone VI* (PG-13) Eves. 7:10 9:10 Mats. S/S 1:10 3:10
Lethal Terminator (R) M-F 12:30 6:50 9:45 S/S 12:30 4:00 6:50 9:45	*Wilderness Trail* (PG) Eves. 7:25 9:30 Mats. S/S 1:25 3:25
Jurassic Park II (PG-13) M-F 1:30 7:20 9:50 S/S 1:00 3:50 7:20 9:50	*Alien Planet* (R) Eves. 7:00 9:10 Mats. S/S 1:20 3:30

MOVIE LISTINGS

1. What do the following abbreviations in the listings stand for?

   (a) M-F _____

   (b) S/S _____

   (c) Eves. _____

   (d) Mats. _____

2. Which movie or movies would you choose to go to in the following situations? (You don't want to come in late.)

   (a) You can't get to the theater until 1:25 Monday afternoon.

   _____

   _____

   (b) You want to take your five-year-old niece to a G-rated movie.

   _____

   _____

   (c) It's 4:00 on Saturday afternoon.

   _____

   _____

   (d) You want to go to a movie after you get off from work Thursday evening at 9:40.

   _____

   _____

   (e) You want to see a movie rated PG.

   _____

   _____

(continued)

MOVIE LISTINGS (CONTINUED)

(f) You like violent action movies, so you're looking for something that's R-rated.

_____

_____

(g) It's Sunday afternoon at 1:00.

_____

_____

(h) You want to go to the first movie on Tuesday that starts after 6:30.

_____

_____

What Do You Think?

3. What do the ratings stand for? (The ratings are the letters in parentheses after the movie title.)

_____

_____

4. Do you think movie ratings are a good guide to a movie's contents? Why or why not?

_____

_____

5. Do you think movie ratings are useful? Why or why not?

_____

_____

6. Do ratings affect your choice of what movie to see? Why or why not?

_____

_____

Rental Rates

$3 for first movie
$2 for each additional movie
$1 for all kids' movies

Tuesday is 2-for-1 Day!
Rent two movies—the lower-priced
movie is free.
Only one of the two movies may
be a new release.

Thursday is Dollar Day!
All non-new releases are $1
New releases are $2

Nintendo Rates

Same as movie rates.

Tuesday is 2-for-1 Day!
Rent two Nintendo games for the
price of one.
$1 for each extra new Nintendo release.

Wednesday is Nintendo Day!
All games are $1
Deck and two games—$5
Nintendo or Sega Deck
with two games—$10

Movie Certificates

VCR and two movies—$10
$1 for each additional movie
$35.00 for 20 movies

$25 for 10 movies
$30 for 15 movies

Note: All tapes due back by 6 P.M. the day after rental.
Use our night drop slot for after-hour returns.

VCR's: We service most types of VCR's. VCR cleaning—$25
Proper identification is required to rent a VCR. We may also require a deposit.

VIDEO STORE

1. Write **True** or **False** next to each of the following statements about this video store's policy.

   _____ (a) On Tuesday, you can rent a second Nintendo game for free.

   _____ (b) On Thursday, you can rent a movie for $1.

   _____ (c) Rentals are due back by 6 P.M. two days after you rent them.

   _____ (d) You need some type of identification, like a driver's license, to rent a VCR.

   _____ (e) On Tuesday, you can rent two new releases for the price of one.

   _____ (f) This store can repair your VCR.

   _____ (g) Kids' movies cost $1 each to rent.

   _____ (h) Nintendo deck and two movies cost $10 to rent at all times.

2. How much do you have to pay to rent each of the following?

   (a) A VCR and two movies: _____

   (b) A VCR and three movies: _____

   (c) Two movies on Tuesday: _____

   (d) Two movies on Monday: _____

   (e) Two movies (non-new) on Thursday: _____

   (f) Nintendo deck and two games on Wednesday: _____

   (g) Nintendo deck and two games on Saturday: _____

   (h) Two non-new Nintendo games on Tuesday: _____

(continued)

VIDEO STORE (CONTINUED)

What Do You Think?

3. Why does the store require "proper identification" to rent a VCR?

_____

_____

_____

_____

_____

Why doesn't it require "proper identification" to rent videos or games?

_____

_____

_____

_____

4. The store says it "may" require a deposit. Why? When do you think the store would require one?

_____

_____

_____

_____

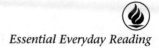

Choosing the Right Film Speed

100 Speed	Use when there's plenty of available light and slow-moving or stationary subjects. Excellent for enlargements.
200 Speed	Use on sunny or bright cloudy days. Excellent results in general daylight or when using flash. Good choice for most outdoor shots.
400 Speed	Use when photographing in lower light levels or when using high shutter speeds to stop action.
1600 Speed	Best choice for existing light. Lets you use higher shutter speeds to stop fast action. Provides greater versatility with telephoto and zoom lenses.

Loading Film: Load and unload camera in subdued light according to camera instructions.

Flash Exposure: See the instructions for electronic flash unit or camera.

Processing: Have film processed promptly after exposure or process it yourself (see your photo dealer).

Developing Your Film

Free Prints or Free Film: Check the box of your choice. If no box is checked, you will receive double 4" × 6" prints. See posted list for prices of each selection.

☐ 4" × 6" double prints (second set free)	☐ 4" × 6" double prints in album ($1.99 extra)
☐ 4" × 6" single prints (plus free film)	☐ 4" × 6" single prints in album (99¢ extra)
☐ 3½" × 5" double prints (second set free)	☐ 3½" × 5" single prints (plus free film)

Choose Speed and Type for free film:

☐ 35 mm/100   ☐ 35 mm/200   ☐ 35 mm/400   ☐ 110

Special! Your photos on floppy disk only $3.99 more for up to 27 exposures (35 mm film). Check format desired:

☐ DOS/Windows   ☐ Macintosh   ☐ Power Mac

FILM — USING AND DEVELOPING

1. What speed film should you use for the following conditions?

   (a) In general daylight _____

   (b) In existing light, with zoom lens _____

   (c) In bright daylight with non-moving subjects _____

   (d) For lower light levels _____

   (e) For photos to be enlarged _____

   (f) For fast action _____

2. Write **True** or **False** for each of these statements.

   _____ (a) Load film into the camera away from bright light.

   _____ (b) Only a photo shop can develop this film.

   _____ (c) You can use a flash with this film.

3. What boxes could you check if you want the following:

   (a) Double prints at no extra cost? _____

   (b) Free film? _____

   (c) Prints in an album? _____

   (d) Prints on a computer disk? _____

What Do You Think?

4. Which would be the best film for your camera, to use in a variety of picture-taking conditions?

   _____

5. Why might you order 4" × 6" rather than the cheaper $3\frac{1}{2}$" × 5" prints?

   _____

   _____

6. Which would you choose, double prints or free film? Why?

   _____

   _____

VIDEOCASSETTE CARE

■ By following these few simple guidelines, you will help to ensure that the videocassette collection at our public library will remain in good condition for all patrons to use and enjoy. We appreciate your cooperation.

1. Video equipment is harmed by moisture that forms when temperatures change. All videocassettes should be at room temperature for two hours or longer before being used.

2. Handle videocassettes carefully. Above all, never touch the tape surface itself or attempt to mend a tape. Dust, dirt, or fingerprints can cause deterioration in signal quality.

3. Keep videocassettes away from direct sunlight or heat such as a car parked in the sun or a radiator. Never put tapes on top of a television, VCR, or stereo speakers. Do not take them through a magnetic security system.

4. Store videocassettes in their protective containers.

5. Please rewind all videocassettes completely before removing them from the VCR.

6. The videocassettes are in VHS format, so be sure your equipment is compatible.

7. Dirty VCR's can cause poor picture quality and can damage tapes. Your machine should be cleaned periodically (at least once or twice a year)— this does make a difference. Commercial cleaning cassettes are available, or a VCR service person can clean your machine.

8. If your picture is not clear or rolls, try adjusting the tracking switch on your machine.

9. If you find a tape damaged or unplayable, please let the Audiovisual Department know immediately.

VIDEOCASSETTE CARE

1. Put a check mark next to each thing below that you **should** do to take good care of videocassettes. Cross out each thing you should **not** do.

_____ (a) Do not leave videocassette in a car parked in the sun.

_____ (b) Be sure to rewind videocassette completely after you've played it.

_____ (c) Keep videocassette ready for use on top of your VCR or TV set.

_____ (d) Clean your VCR once or twice a year.

_____ (e) Keep videocassette at room temperature for at least two hours before playing it.

_____ (f) If you damage a tape, mend it.

_____ (g) If videocassette jams and won't run, push tape surface gently forward with your fingers.

_____ (h) Keep videocassette away from radiators.

_____ (i) Keep videocassette in the VCR, not in the container you bring it home in.

_____ (j) You can clean your VCR yourself with a cleaning cassette.

2. If the tape doesn't play correctly, can you do anything about it yourself?

If so, what? _____

_____

_____

What Do You Think?

3. What is a "magnetic security system"? _____

_____

Where do you most often find one? _____

4. What does VCR stand for? _____

5. Do you think the library will blame or fine you if you return a tape that is damaged or unplayable?

_____

UNIT 8. HEALTH AND PERSONAL CARE

Like household products, personal care products are all different and are used in different ways. Read their directions to be sure you use them correctly. In an emergency, you may have to read very important first aid directions. Practice this kind of reading here. First, get to know some of the vocabulary words in this section, Write the correct word from the following list on the blank next to the word's definition below.

abdomen	consult	ingestion	ointment
accidental	dispense	inhale	persist
administer	effective	lozenge	physician
avoid	exceed	mousse	thrust

_____ 1. To ask for a person's advice or opinion

_____ 2. Producing a desired effect

_____ 3. To keep away from

_____ 4. Taking in, as for digestion

_____ 5. Gel-like product used on the hair for styling

_____ 6. To deal out in portions

_____ 7. To breathe in

_____ 8. Small medicated candy

_____ 9. Doctor

_____ 10. To continue to exist past an expected time

_____ 11. Happening by chance; not planned

_____ 12. Middle part of the body

_____ 13. To push or drive with force

_____ 14. A soothing, healing substance rubbed on the skin

_____ 15. To give a dose of medicine

_____ 16. To go beyond a limit; overdo

Essential Everyday Reading

Relieves:

- **Cold Sores / Fever Blisters / Sun Blisters:** Relieves pain, itching, and discomfort. Apply at first sign a cold sore is developing (tingling, pain, itching), repeating application as indicated below.

- **Cracked / Severely Dry Lips:** Moistens and softens.

- **Minor Skin Injuries:** Abrasions, cuts, scrapes, burns, razor nicks, and chafed or irritated skin.

- **Insect Bites:** Mosquitoes, black flies, sand fleas, chiggers.

Directions:

Rub ointment gently into affected area, three to four times a day.

Warnings:

For external use only. Avoid using near eyes. In case of eye contact, flush thoroughly with water and obtain medical attention. In case of accidental ingestion, seek professional assistance or contact a poison control center immediately. Keep this and all drugs out of the reach of children.

Caution:

Not for prolonged use. Not to be applied over large areas of the body. In case of redness, swelling, or pain that persists more than seven days, or if rash or infection develops, discontinue use and consult a physician. Do not bandage if applied to fingers or toes. Do not use on deep or puncture wounds or serious burns. This product should be used by only one person.

COLD SORE OINTMENT

1. What three kinds of lip sores is this product mainly intended to treat?

   _____

   _____

2. What other lip condition does this product also treat?

   _____

   _____

3. What kinds of minor skin injuries does this product also treat?

   _____

   _____

4. What kinds of insect bites does this product treat?

   _____

   _____

5. What are the early signs of a cold sore or fever blister?

   _____

   _____

6. How often should you apply this product to the sore area?

   _____

   _____

7. What should you do if you get some of this ointment in your eye?

   _____

   _____

(continued)

COLD SORE OINTMENT (CONTINUED)

8. What should you do if your little brother eats some of this ointment?

   _____

   _____

9. What kinds of sores or injuries should you **not** use this ointment for?

   (a) _____

   (b) _____

   (c) _____

   (d) _____

   (e) _____

   (f) _____

What Do You Think?

10. The instructions say that this ointment is "not for prolonged use." How long is "prolonged"?

    _____

    _____

    For how many days do you think you could use this ointment?

    _____

    _____

11. Why do you think the instructions say that this product should be used by only one person?

    _____

    _____

| Extra Control ■ Extra Body and Fullness ■ Soft to Touch |

Our extra-body mousse uses an airy foam that mixes easily and thoroughly through your hair.

- Gives your hair extra hold and control

- Adds extra body and volume even to fine, limp hair

- Special formula conditions and helps protect hair from drying out and styling stress

- No flaking, stickiness, or buildup

- Leaves your hair looking beautifully glowing, with a soft natural touch

Directions: Apply to shampooed, towel-dried hair. Shake can well. Turn upside down. Press button and dispense a golf-ball-sized mound of foam into palm of hand (more for longer hair). Work lightly and evenly throughout damp hair. Do not rinse. Style as desired. Apply to dry hair for control or quick styling touch-up.

■ Contains 25 to 30 Applications ■

Warning: Avoid spraying in eyes. Contents under pressure. Do not puncture or incinerate. Do not store at temperatures above 120°F. Do not use near fire or flame. Keep out of reach of children. Use only as directed. Intentional misuse by deliberately concentrating and inhaling can be harmful or fatal.

Satisfaction guaranteed or your money back.

HAIRSTYLING MOUSSE

1. Put a check (✓) next to each thing below that you **should** do while using this mousse. Cross out each thing you should **not** do.

   _____ (a) Don't worry about spraying in your eyes.

   _____ (b) Apply after shampooing your hair.

   _____ (c) Hold can upside down.

   _____ (d) Do not shake can.

   _____ (e) Apply golf-ball-sized mound of foam.

   _____ (f) Use more foam for longer hair.

   _____ (g) Burn can when it is empty.

   _____ (h) Spread mousse all through hair.

   _____ (i) Rinse mousse out after three minutes.

   _____ (j) Feel free to inhale contents of can.

2. How many times should you expect to be able to use this can of mousse?

   _____

3. Is this a good choice for you if your hair is hard to control and style?

   _____

   How can you tell if it's a good choice?

   _____

4. According to the can, how will your hair look after you use this product?

   _____

What Do You Think?

5. What would be the best way to dispose of this can?

   _____

6. What if you don't like the way this mousse works on your hair?

   _____

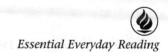

Sore Throat Lozenges
for fast temporary relief of minor sore throat pain

Tamper Resistant: Product inside sealed in plastic for your protection. Do not use if blister package is damaged.

Indications: For temporary relief of occasional minor throat and mouth irritation, including dry, scratchy throat.

Directions: Adults and children five years of age and older: Allow one lozenge to dissolve slowly in the mouth. May be repeated every two hours as needed or as directed by a dentist or physician.

Warnings: If sore throat is severe, persists for more than two days, is accompanied or followed by fever, headache, rash, nausea, vomiting, or breathing difficulty, consult a physician promptly. If sore throat symptoms do not improve in seven days, see your dentist or physician promptly. Do not administer to children under five years of age unless directed by physician or dentist. Do not exceed recommended dosage. Keep this and all drugs out of the reach of children. In case of accidental overdose, seek professional assistance or contact a Poison Control Center immediately. As with any drug, if you are pregnant or nursing a baby, seek the advice of a health professional before using this product.

Storage: Store at room temperature, below 86°F (30°C). Protect contents from humidity and moisture. Use by expiration date printed on package.

THROAT LOZENGES

1. Write **True** or **False** next to each statement below.

____ (a) These lozenges are perfectly safe for children under the age of five.

____ (b) Be sure the package seal is not broken before you use any lozenges.

____ (c) Swallow lozenge right away.

____ (d) Wait seven days for your sore throat to clear up before calling your doctor.

____ (e) Take a lozenge every two hours if you need to.

____ (f) Take these lozenges to treat headache or nausea.

____ (g) Talk to your doctor if you have a fever or rash along with your sore throat.

____ (h) Take the lozenges to make a dry, scratchy throat feel better.

____ (i) Talk to a doctor or other medical person before taking these lozenges if you are pregnant.

____ (j) An overdose of these lozenges is nothing to worry about.

2. When should you **call** your doctor about your sore throat, according to the lozenge package?

_____

_____

_____

3. When should you **see** your doctor about your sore mouth, according to the lozenge package?

_____

_____

What Do You Think?

4. Where should you **not** store these lozenges?

_____

5. Why shouldn't you use the lozenges if the plastic seal is damaged?

_____

FIRST AID FOR CHOKING VICTIMS

[Restaurants often have posters telling how to give first aid to someone who is choking. Imagine if someone you were with was choking. You'd have to read these directions very quickly so you could save your friend from choking to death!]

■ First, decide if the person is choking or not. A conscious person whose airway is blocked:

- Can't breathe, speak, or cough

- May clutch her or his throat

- May turn cyanotic (bluish, or darker)

■ If someone collapses but is conscious, ask, "Can you speak?" If not, the person probably is choking. Take action immediately. Use the Heimlich maneuver to remove the object from the victim's throat.

1. **If the victim is standing or sitting:** Stand behind the victim. Wrap your arms around the victim's waist. Make a fist with one hand. Place the thumb side of that fist against the victim's abdomen, slightly above the navel and below the rib cage. Grasp your fist with your other hand. Press the fist into the victim's abdomen with a sharp upward thrust. Repeat the thrust several times if necessary.

2. **If the victim is lying down:** Turn the victim onto his or her back. Straddle the victim, on your knees. Put one of your hands on top of the other. Put the heel of the bottom hand in the middle of the victim's abdomen, slightly above the navel and below the rib cage. Position yourself so your shoulders are directly above the victim's abdomen. Press into the victim's abdomen with a sharp upward thrust. Repeat the thrust several times if necessary. (Be sure to turn the victim to the side and clear out her or his mouth if the victim vomits.)

3. **If you are alone and choking:** Perform the Heimlich maneuver on yourself. Press your own fist, thumb side first, into your abdomen with a quick upward thrust. Or press your abdomen quickly and hard against the edge of sink, hard chair, or railing.

■ If the choking victim is an infant or small child, make the upward thrust less hard.

111   *Essential Everyday Reading*

FIRST AID FOR CHOKING VICTIMS

1. Choking can kill a person! But before you try to rescue someone from choking, what do you have to do first?

   _____

   _____

2. Put a check mark next to the person who is choking in these scenes.

   _____ (a) A woman is coughing uncontrollably and can't talk.

   _____ (b) A man can only take short gasps of air.

   _____ (c) A girl can't talk to you, and can't cough or breathe at all either.

   _____ (d) A toddler having a temper tantrum is holding his breath.

3. Number these steps in the correct order.

   _____ Press your fist into the victim's abdomen with a sharp upward thrust.

   _____ Ask the victim if she can speak.

   _____ Wrap your arms around the victim.

   _____ Place your fist against the victim's abdomen.

   _____ Stand behind the victim.

   _____ Repeat the thrust if necessary.

   _____ Make a fist with one hand.

4. What must you do for a victim who is lying down, in addition to the Heimlich maneuver?

   _____

   _____

   _____

   _____

(continued)

Essential Everyday Reading

FIRST AID FOR CHOKING VICTIMS *(CONTINUED)*

5. How can you rescue yourself from choking?

_____

_____

_____

_____

What Do You Think?

6. Should all restaurant workers be trained in the Heimlich maneuver?

_____

Why or why not? _____

_____

_____

7. Have you been trained in the Heimlich maneuver?

_____

_____

If not, do you plan to be?

_____

_____

Where could you get training?

_____

_____

_____

Unit 9. Popular Press

Maybe you don't **need** to read articles in popular magazines and newspapers about things like sports, weather, and personal advice. But it's an entertaining and interesting way to relax in your spare time. So have some fun reading this section, and keep on developing your essential reading skills!

TABLE OF CONTENTS

Features

Fashion

Food and Health

In Every Issue

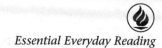

TABLE OF CONTENTS

1. If you want to read about clothing, which section of the contents should you look at?

_____

_____

2. If you're interested in knowing more about what you eat and how you feel, which section of the contents should you look at?

_____

_____

3. If you want to read one of this month's special articles, which section of the contents should you look at?

_____

_____

4. Does this magazine have a story about teen suicide in every issue?

_____

_____

5. Does this magazine have reviews of music, movies, and books in every issue?

_____

_____

6. If you want to read a short story that's **not** about something that really happened, which article would you go to?

_____

_____

(continued)

TABLE OF CONTENTS (CONTINUED)

7. If you're interested in cars, which article would especially appeal to you?

   _____

   _____

8. If you're about to go shopping for some new summer clothes, which articles might you read first?

   _____

   _____

9. If you want to read all the articles about physical health, which ones would they be?

   _____

   _____

   _____

What Do You Think?

10. How could this magazine help if you had a personal or health problem you didn't know what to do about?

    _____

    _____

    _____

11. What kinds of readers do you think this magazine appeals to?

    _____

    _____

    _____

■ **Dear Anna:** I've been going with this girl for four months. Now her ex-boyfriend tells me she's been cheating on me. Should I believe him?—*Wondering*

● **Dear Wondering:** The ex-boyfriend may be jealous about your relationship with his ex-girlfriend. He could be telling you this story just to make trouble. Tell your girlfriend what her ex has said to you. If she says it's not true, and you feel she's being sincere, believe her. Forget about the story unless you get proof that it's true.

■ **Dear Anna:** My parents insist on a 9:00 curfew for me even though I'm 16! I'm very frustrated and angry that they're ruining my social life! What can I do?—*Boiling Mad*

● **Dear Boiling:** First, calm down. Then approach your parents when both you and they are relaxed. Tell them you want to discuss your curfew with them. Explain that you feel mature and responsible enough to be allowed to stay out later on weekends. Point out that you need to be given more responsibility for what you do now that you are older. If they still object, ask them to tell you ways in which you can show them that you're responsible and can be trusted. They should come around.

■ **Dear Anna:** I'm terrible at sports and always feel like a klutz when I try to play. This makes me feel like a social outcast. Help!—*Not a Jock*

● **Dear Not:** You may have no choice about sports if you've got phys ed classes in school. But there's lots more to sports than team play like football, basketball, or softball. Try some individual physical activities, like hiking, biking, swimming, or aerobics. You'll feel better physically, and your coordination and self-image will improve.

ASK ANNA

1. Who does Anna think may be jealous?

   _____

   _____

2. Who does Anna think "Wondering" ought to believe?

   _____

   _____

3. How is "Boiling Mad" supposed to convince her or his parents to allow a later curfew?

   _____

   _____

   _____

4. What individual sports does Anna suggest for "Not a Jock"?

   _____

   _____

5. What benefits will these individual sports bring to "Not a Jock," according to Anna?

   _____

   _____

6. How can "Not a Jock" avoid team sports, according to Anna?

   _____

   _____

(continued)

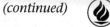

ASK ANNA *(CONTINUED)*

What Do You Think?

7. Why does the column use names like "Wondering" and "Boiling Mad" instead of names like Leon or Vanessa?

   _____

   _____

   _____

8. What do you think is a reasonable curfew, if any, for a 16-year-old?

   _____

   _____

   _____

9. What might happen if "Boiling Mad" talked to his or her parents while he or she was very angry about the curfew?

   _____

   _____

   _____

10. What advice would you give to these letter writers?

   _____

   _____

   _____

   _____

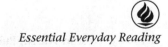

Libra (Sept. 23 to Oct. 22)
Family hassles are likely in mid-month. Stay calm and play peacemaker. Tensions will ease by month's end.

Scorpio (Oct. 23 to Nov. 21)
Venus favors your love life this month. Now is the time to encourage that budding relationship. It may turn to romance!

Sagittarius (Nov. 22 to Dec. 21)
Pay attention to money matters this month. Don't take any chances. Hold back on big purchases.

Capricorn (Dec. 22 to Jan. 19)
A longtime friendship could develop troubles now. Be patient, and don't let any disagreements blow up and out of control.

Aquarius (Jan. 20 to Feb. 18)
This is your month to relax and have fun! Parties, dates, and plans with friends are all in the picture.

Pisces (Feb. 19 to March 20)
Your energy levels are high this month. So tackle some of those projects you've been putting off. Try to put the brakes on, though, before you get in too deep.

Aries (Mar. 21 to Apr. 19)
A loved one is feeling particularly sensitive. Now is the time to talk things out. If you express your real feelings, your partner will, too.

Taurus (Apr. 20 to May 20)
Studies and work may seem especially difficult this month. Hang in there. The hassles will ease up soon. Contact with an old friend will help.

Gemini (May 21 to June 21)
You may be moody and tense early in the month. But your usual social nature will reappear quickly. Hold off on any relationship changes until you're back to normal.

Cancer (June 22 to July 22)
This is a good month to travel. Both short trips and long ones will bring you satisfaction. A long-awaited letter will arrive.

Leo (July 23 TO Aug. 22)
Bold moves will bring results now! Call that person you've been thinking about. Apply for that job you think you can't get. Chances are you'll succeed.

Virgo (Aug. 23 to Sept. 22)
Express your artistic nature this month. Be creative! Don't be surprised to find yourself on the phone a lot. Your friends will seek you out.

Essential Everyday Reading

MONTHLY HOROSCOPE

1. Which sign of the zodiac would apply to someone with the following birth date?

   (a) January 6 _____

   (b) September 23 _____

   (c) April 1 _____

   (d) February 26 _____

   (e) July 21 _____

   (f) September 18 _____

2. Which monthly horoscope matches each statement below? Write the zodiac sign on the blank for each.

   (a) The month starts off with you moody and tense. _____

   (b) Be careful with your money. _____

   (c) Take a trip. _____

   (d) This is a good month for romance. _____

   (e) Be bold! _____

   (f) Go out with your friends a lot. _____

   (g) You're likely to have problems with your work. _____

   (h) Create something artistic. _____

What Do You Think?

3. Do horoscopes make any sense? Can signs of the zodiac actually have any effect on a person's life?

   _____

   _____

   _____

WEATHER FORECAST

Extended Forecast

Friday:	**Saturday:**	**Sunday:**
Chance of showers north and east. Fair southwest. High in the low 80's, low in the mid-50s.	Chance of showers north and east. Clouds, then hazy sun southwest. Fog along the coast. High in the upper 70's to mid-80's. Low in the upper 50s.	Fair north and east. Morning sun southwest, scattered showers and thunderstorms afternoon. High in the mid-80's. Low in the mid-60's.

Two-Day Forecast

- Today, Wednesday, both southern and northern parts of the state will see rain in the morning, becoming mostly cloudy with scattered showers by afternoon. High in the mid-70's with moderate winds.

- Tonight, clouds will begin to disperse in the south, with the threat of showers ending after midnight. Low in the lower 60's. North, skies will remain cloudy, with a good chance of scattered showers and thunderstorms. Low in the upper 50's.

- Thursday, becoming partly sunny by midmorning in the south, with a chance of thunderstorms by late afternoon. High between 75 and 80, with light southwest winds. North, cloudy in the morning, followed by late clearing. High in the mid-70's.

Almanac

Sun rises	5:31 A.M.
Sun sets	8:03 P.M.
Hours of daylight	14 hr. 32 min.
Moon rises	7:47 P.M.
Moon sets	5:45 A.M.
High tide	noon
Low tide	5:46 A.M., 5:55 P.M.

WEATHER FORECAST

1. For each weather condition described below, tell which day of the week it applies to. Also tell the time of day (morning, afternoon, night) if the forecast mentions that.

   (a) _____ Fog along the coast.

   (b) _____ The first sun in the south.

   (c) _____ Chance of thunderstorms in the north.

   (d) _____ First clearing in the north.

   (e) _____ Fair in the north and east.

   (f) _____ Clouds followed by hazy sun in the southwest.

   (g) _____ Chance of thunderstorms in the south and southwest.

   (h) _____ Rain.

   (i) _____ Rain clouds break up in the south.

2. What day is expected to be the warmest? _____

3. What day is expected to have the lowest low temperature? _____

4. If you wanted to dig clams at low tide, when would you do it?

   _____

   _____

   _____

What Do You Think?

5. Study a weather map. Learn what its symbols mean. How can a weather map help you to plan your outdoor activities?

   _____

   _____

   _____

6. Why would people want to know what time the moon rises and sets?

   _____

   _____

Stress Test

■ Stress can ruin your life. You can't create a stress-free life yourself. But you **can** learn to cope with stress and make it less...stressful. How effective are your stress-coping strategies? Find out by taking this stress test. Put a check next to the answer that fits you the best.

I. You have two tests and a term paper due on the same day next week. You:

_____ (a) Spend most of your time worrying about how to get it all done.

_____ (b) Make a study schedule and stick to it.

_____ (c) Know you can't get it all done, so put it out of your mind.

II. Your best friend won't talk to you. You:

_____ (a) Sit alone in your room for hours brooding about losing your friend.

_____ (b) Send notes to your friend saying you need to talk about what's wrong.

_____ (c) Pretend you don't care.

III. Your parents argue a lot. You:

_____ (a) Listen to every argument and worry that they'll get divorced.

_____ (b) Try to talk to them about it sometimes, and keep yourself busy with studying and outside activities most of the time.

_____ (c) Put on your headphones and ignore them.

Rate Your Answers

- If you answer (a) to two out of three, you're letting the stressful situation eat you up. You're not doing anything to cope with the stress.

- If you answer (c) to two out of three, you're not coping with the stress at all. You're just trying to pretend it doesn't exist. But it does.

- If you answer (b) to two out of three, you're taking sensible, practical steps to deal with the stress and to lessen its effects on you.

HOW WELL DO YOU COPE WITH STRESS?

What Do You Think?

1. How well do you cope with stress? _____

_____

_____

2. Take the stress test yourself. How do your answers rate? _____

_____

_____

3. Write down another stressful situation and try to come up with three ways of responding to it.

_____

_____

_____

_____

_____

_____

_____

_____

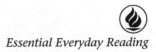